The Arrow Tree: Healing from L

Phyllis Weliver was in the first wave to
from the city to a woodland cottage
regain health, Weliver reflects o.. ... process of integrating
mind/body health with the natural world. As she recovers from long-
haul COVID, the author draws inspiration from forest bathing,
traditional Odawa and Ojibwe culture, ancient Chinese philosophy,
and British and American literature.

While this memoir may be of special interest to those dealing with
chronic illness, Weliver's narrative ultimately addresses how we might
all mend from the bruising pace of modern life.

About the author

Twice funded by the National Endowment for the Humanities for her
scholarly work, Phyllis Weliver is Professor of English at Saint Louis
University and Fellow of Gladstone's Library in Wales. Her previous
books include *Mary Gladstone and the Victorian Salon* (Cambridge
University Press).

Also by Phyllis Weliver

Mary Gladstone and the Victorian Salon:
Music, Literature, Liberalism

The Musical Crowd in English Fiction, 1840–1910:
Class, Culture and Nation

Women Musicians in Victorian Fiction, 1860–1900:
Representations of Music, Science and Gender in the Leisured Home

The Arrow Tree

Healing from Long COVID

Phyllis Weliver

EXEAT IMPRINTS

First published 2021 by

EXEAT IMPRINTS
PO Box 247, Pacific, MO, 63069, USA
www.exeatimprints.com

EXEAT IMPRINTS is the global imprint of Exeat Media, LLC

Library of Congress Control Number: 2021909428

ISBN 978-1-7364243-1-5 Paperback

For my readers

Contents

Acknowledgements

HE *Arrow Tree* painting and cover design are by Emily Bracale, an artist who lives and works in Maine. The Exeat Imprints logo was printed by Robert Lowing using type from Henry Dyer Lowing, our three-times great grandfather and founder in 1880 of the Linesville Tribune newspaper. The half-title page and matching drop caps at the beginning of chapters were printed using the same family press.

Most of the book's content comes from my personal journals and recollections of events. A small excerpt from the preface and another from Appendix A first circulated publicly on Facebook.

In the process of writing about long COVID, I have grown to understand it within a longer history of epidemics. I am persuaded by Felicity Callard, Professor of Human Geography at the University of Glasgow, who situates long-haul coronavirus in terms of the terrible neglect and misunderstanding experienced by those individuals with other post-viral conditions such as myalgic encephalomyelitis/chronic fatigue syndrome (ME/CFS) where "diagnostic terminology ... focuses on effects in the absence of knowledge about cause" (731). The "coronavirus pandemic will likely," Callard argues, "end up being slotted into a ... series of epidemic outbreaks that are positioned as having precipitated many cases of ME" (730). My focus is on long COVID because it is what I have experienced, but hopefully there is mutual advantage to raising awareness about any of these syndromes. Jamie Seltzer, Scientific Consultant on Stanford University's ME/CFS project, and her colleagues put it this way: "'What is it going to take for researchers to take ME seriously?' The morbid answer, they hypothesized, was a pandemic" (Ducharme; my thanks to Callard for this source).

(In)visibility is partially a product of nomenclature, or the act of naming. Because COVID stands for <u>co</u>rona<u>vi</u>rus <u>d</u>isease, it is capitalized when indicating the 2019 novel coronavirus according to MLA Style, which this book follows. Long COVID, however, does not seem to have been standardized by dictionaries and style guides. The *Oxford English Dictionary* and *Merriam-Webster* both leave it out, for example. Common usage reveals variation: the twitter hashtags #LongCovid and #CountLongCovid remove all but the initial capitalization; the Body Politic COVID-19 Support Group retains the full capitalization. For this book, I decided to capitalize COVID in "long COVID" because of the MLA style treatment of COVID-19 and because the font visually indicates the connection to the acute phase of the virus. In my experience, there's nothing "post" about long COVID. I refer here to the medical names for the condition: Chronic Post-COVID Syndrome and Post-Acute COVID-19 Syndrome. Because of the general practice of avoiding capitalization in disease names except when they include proper nouns or acronyms, I do not capitalize "long." These formatting decisions acknowledge and validate the patient experience of a real illness.

I wish to express my gratitude to those people who kindly offered feedback on drafts of this book. Dale Chandler and his niece, Valerie Chandler, both citizens of the Little River Band of Ottawa Indians of Manistee and Mason counties in northern Michigan, thoughtfully responded about aspects of their living culture. Valerie formerly served as the Little River Band's Historic Preservation Coordinator. Dale's mother, Margaret Chandler, played a vital role in helping their tribe to become federally reaffirmed in 1994. The other two federally reaffirmed Odawa tribes in Michigan are the Little Traverse Bay Bands of Odawa Indians and the Grand Traverse Band of Ottawa and Chippewa Indians.

Votes of confidence on an early excerpt of this book by poet and novelist Jack Driscoll and by poet David Walker were key to my decision to publish. Laurie Bayless, Abigail Ellsworth, Devin Johnston, Claire Cowley, Meirion Hughes, Debbie Grossman, Jenny Bourne Taylor and David Walker helpfully read and responded to a full draft. Mark A. Clark's enthusiastic response to the manuscript meant a lot to me.

My knowledge of Odawa and Ojibwe culture comes from a lifetime of curiosity and deep respect. Growing up in the northwest of Michigan's lower peninsula, it is impossible to miss the widely-circulated "Legend of the Sleeping Bear." During my convalescence, I enjoyed reading those legends and area histories approved by tribal elders for publication in books and online. Where possible, I gravitated toward the narratives of northern Michigan bands for, as Odawa and Ojibwe elder Simon Otto cautions, "Stories and legends from the Indian world are often similar but they are not told the same" (page 3). Federally recognized Odawa tribes in Michigan inhabit reservation areas in Antrim, Benzie, Charlevoix, Grand Traverse, Leelanau, Mason and Manistee counties. These areas comprise over 150 miles of contiguous northern Lake Michigan shoreline, with reservation lands accounting for approximately 340 square miles within these counties. I appreciate the Grand Traverse Band of Ottawa and Chippewa Indians for putting me in touch with their "Tree Guy," Tom Callison, who generously spoke with me at length about bent trees in northwestern lower Michigan.

For acupuncture, I am indebted for my understanding to discussions during treatments with board certified acupuncturists, Abigail Ellsworth and Afua Bromley (also one of the ten-member Board of Commissioners for the National Certification Commission for Acupuncture and Oriental Medicine). Acupuncture has been part of my health regime for over a decade now, including during my recovery from long COVID. I have also explored the work of influential acupuncturists such as Giovanni Maciocia and Wang Ju-Yi.

For their support during this difficult time, I would like to thank Toby Benis, David Bowman, Emily Bracale, Hal and Hiroko Bush, Miriam Campbell, Zöe Clyde-Watson, Brian Evans-Jones, Rebecca Ford, Jessica Harbeson, Torrie Hester, Ericka Hofmeyer, Malcolm Jones, Donna LaVoie, Jennifer Lowe, Paulita Neal, Del and Ruth Proctor, Donald Stump, the Urban family, Fiona Wardle and Andy Willinger. There are many more people in my extended community who reached out to offer care in social media posts and private communications. I am deeply grateful to all.

Finally, and most importantly, without my family's love, understanding and assistance, I simply could not have healed as much as I have done. Bruce, Hollis, Mom and Dad, my gratitude runs so much deeper than words. It is as much a part of my essence as is this book. Thank you.

Preface

I am one of the millions who survived COVID-19 only to develop long-haul symptoms. Long COVID or Chronic Post-COVID Syndrome (also known as Post-Acute COVID-19 Syndrome) is defined as having symptoms consistent with COVID-19 that last beyond the first twelve weeks.

I first became ill with COVID-19 in late March 2020, probably having come into contact with the virus as I departed England on an international flight to the United States. At that time, the United Kingdom had just been declared a Moderate Risk for COVID-19 on the WHO's Risk Assessment rankings, or a Level 2 country. In an abundance of caution, my family and I went into quarantine for a fortnight immediately upon my arrival at St. Louis's Lambert Airport in Missouri, about 300 miles south of Chicago on the Mississippi River. We all fell ill on the fourteenth day of our isolation.

During my medical leave, friends regularly asked, "What are you doing during your convalescence?" "Are you working, or following doctor's orders?" Knowing my workaholic tendency, one friend suggested in all seriousness that I learn to watch the grass grow.

Well, I've done a lot of just that from a hammock strung between two pines. For me, physical health began to return as a direct response to living in and reflecting upon an area of outstanding natural beauty. This lifestyle and the desire to get better led me to reassess how I had been living and to grapple with finding another way. What is a life worth living? Repeatedly, my acupuncturist and I observed that as personal insights occurred, my physical health made a corresponding leap forward, even before the needling session began. The acupuncture supported my inner work; it facilitated the next step rather than being the cure. I'm emerging from chronic COVID a different, healthier version of me.

These writings were vital to my recuperative process. Abigail, my acupuncturist in Michigan, reflected back to me recently that writing was in fact the most important piece of my treatment; it was a self-prescription. From friends in the fields of medical humanities and music therapy, I already knew that the arts were therapeutic. However, it took physical weakness truly to comprehend this lesson. I've journaled since I was a teenager, but my attempts to heal long COVID by daily writing were more creative. Instead of simply accounting for the events of the day, my journaling tapped therapeutic energy by creatively contemplating the natural world. I thought symbolically, while also utilizing other literary techniques to craft prose that would pay homage to my beautiful surroundings. The English Romantic poet Samuel Taylor Coleridge understood this process as what it means to be human: to think metaphysically and to express our intuitions through artistry.

Symbols, of course, are dependent upon context for their interpretation. I've integrated my experiences in the natural world with considerations of holistic health, drawing particular inspiration from the beliefs of the Odawa and Ojibwe people: the original, ongoing and future stewards of Michigan where I grew up and where I lived as I recovered. Meanings from ancient Chinese philosophies also resonated with me because they underlay my acupuncture treatments and because we formed our family through international adoption from China. Finally, as a professor of English, my thinking is steeped in British and American literature. I publish academic books that consider what it means to be a human being as expressed in the creative word.

This memoir's topic is humanity as interactive with the amazing fount of positive energy found in the wild and the resulting healthy balance. My method has been to bring together my observations of the natural world with, first, a deeply honest inner assessment and, second, the wisdom of others. This memoir shares perceptions and perspective as it weaves back and forth in the associative processes of a lifetime. Occasional literary citation and analysis arise from my expertise as a literary scholar. Throughout, the words communicate the substance of thought and of being. In writing, I've found a healthier and perhaps truer version of myself.

The Arrow Tree is an account of the recalibration of modern life to prioritize the health of the whole person, and how it has paid off in unexpected and positive ways.

Introduction

What if COVID-19 saved my life?

HE subtitle of this book, "Healing from Long COVID" most obviously indicates a journey to restore physical health after disease. However, it also implies that illness from a mysterious virus provides an opportunity to repair the human being: to heal *because* of long COVID. Without medical answers and easy prescriptions, my path toward physical healing included an attempt at self enlightenment. How might I mend the whole person?

Before contracting COVID-19, I would have introduced myself to you by my occupation: a professor at a research university who specializes in the literature and music of Victorian England.

Now? It is more complex.

I'm a mother, wife, daughter, sister, cousin, aunt, friend and professor from the northwestern tip of Michigan's lower peninsula. My husband, son and I live mostly in St. Louis, Missouri. We also have a summer cottage on land first used by a band of Odawa. I am a Gen-Xer born in the USA and, having lived over a third of my adult life in England, I am also deeply tied to English culture.

What emerged from my process of recovery from long COVID were things that I had not imagined: inner peace and genuine happiness alongside an exponentially reviving physical health. The whole person, according to the *Oxford English Dictionary*, is a term originating as early as 1526. It means "a person considered in all aspects of his or her existence, as physical, intellectual, spiritual, etc." If a human being is considered holistically, then the health of mind, body and spirit are related. As I was finishing *The Arrow Tree*, I came across Basil Johnston's beautiful articulation of the same truth in a book about his *Ojibway Heritage*:

> many medicine men and women knew that many forms of ill health were but outward manifestations and forms of the poor state of inner being. There was a recognition that there was a relationship between the physical well being of a person and his inner well being; illness and inner turmoil.

Consequently, in addition to the application of medicines to hurts, a state of peace had to be instilled in the inner being of a patient. (42)

My approach to self-healing is thus shared by the traditional and living culture of the original people of the land where I grew up.

The essays in this book concentrate in a sort of sequence on individualized elements and aspects of self in relation to the natural world. Lao Tzu understood this approach in the fourth century B.C. as:

The five colours make man's eyes blind;
The five notes make his ears deaf;
The five tastes injure his palate;
...
Therefore he discards the one and takes the other. (XII, 28, 29a)

The five colors are red, blue, yellow, black and white; the musical notes correspond to the pentatonic scale used in ancient Chinese music; and the five tastes are sweet, sour, salty, sharp and bitter. Because Taoism's truths exist outside of language, Tzu presents the tenets of this ancient Chinese philosophy through poems that can seem paradoxical. Readers must find their own understanding through an internal process of puzzling out meaning. The above excerpt might be paraphrased thus: to try to see, hear or taste everything at one time causes a sensory cacophony that can only result in illness. Of course, you cannot have one without the others, but concentrating on a single element at a time brings enjoyment and deeper understanding.

Likewise, each of the following chapters focuses on the health of single areas as symbolized by one or two elements, animals or experiences. These aspects are not actually solitary, but it would be bewildering to try to focus on all areas at the same time. Like the final line of the above citation, each element has value, one by one.

My progression through this book follows the path of my thinking. As I wrote, I kept a slim notebook for each topic and usually had a couple of these little journals going at one time. In them, I observed my surroundings and put myself back together, integrating one element at a time with a sense of the world around me. The chapters thus follow a rough chronology through the seasons, but there is some overlap sequentially. The organization pivots more around exploring aspects of self, including nonlinear associations and memories of my own, and the history of the land itself. Time is thus explored as circling and layering, rather than as a direct, teleological movement between points A and B.

Put another way, I learned the dynamism of the natural world through seeking to understand it. Margaret Noori's dual-language poem, "Waawaateseg (Fireflies)," beautifully expresses this process. It begins with the question in Anishinaabemowin, "Aanii ezhi pagozi dibikgiizis?" In English: "How does moonlight taste?" (line 1). The speaker asks in two languages for guidance in understanding natural light:

> Aanii ezhi ezhichigeyaamba
> ji-nsostaawaag waawaateseg

> What do I need to do
> to understand the fireflies? (3–4)

Understanding can mean both to comprehend and to sympathize with. The poem posits the startling answer in the final stanza:

> N'wii bodewaadiz gonemaa
> miidash tonaanan shkodensan shpemsigong
> anongziibike minajiwong dibikong
> miidash wii baashkaazoying dibishko
> zaagigaabaag ziigwaning.

> Perhaps I will set myself alight
> then place the flames in the sky
> making a river flowing through night
> where explosions echo
> the bursting leaves of Spring. (7–11)

To understand moonlight and fireflies requires mutuality: become the flame and so enlighten the dark. In the process, learning what seemed silent and apart (buds unfurling into leaves; the firefly) can suddenly appear explosive. The natural world has always been there, but its properties are only illuminated through watching and wondering sympathetically about the details. In the process, we enliven ourselves.

There's no doubt that I'm fortunate to have a place away from the city to which to retire in Michigan, to have parents who could help in looking after our young son during my illness, to have a supportive partner in my husband, Bruce, and to have a stable job that allowed me to take a medical leave. I was also lucky to have an extended community who checked in to see how we were doing, and to offer love and encouragement. Many long haulers have found themselves in a very different situation, including loss of employment and abandonment by friends and family. Even so, what I essentially learned is accessible to all: to slow down, look inside and turn to nature, whether it be a tree, an urban park or a country lane.

Note on the Text

The main substance of this book focuses on my healing up to the point when my doctor deemed me sufficiently recovered to return to work. If you would like to know more about the first three months of our illness, about long COVID as it is medically defined, and what happened after I returned to work, please turn to Appendix A. Likewise, Appendix B speaks about Michigan tribal culture and my decisions regarding terminology. Some readers may wish to read this context first before diving into the memoir proper. My choices regarding how to style COVID-19 and long COVID have already been explained in Acknowledgements.

This book follows the MLA system of author/page number in-text citation for prose quotations. For multivolume works, a volume number precedes the page number. Act, scene and line numbers are given for plays. Following the standard literary practice for poems, line numbers are used, except for the *Tao Te Ching* for which chapter and section numbers are given in the manner of D.C. Lau's translation. I use Lau's version except in one instance, which is clearly indicated. The full bibliographic information may be found at the end in Works Cited.

And now we turn to Nature. All these years we have lived beside her, and we have never seen her; and now we open our eyes and look at her.

Olive Schreiner
The Story of an African Farm

1 | Water Lingers

We could never have loved the earth so well if we had had no childhood in it,—if [*sic*] it were not the earth where the same flowers come up again every spring that we used to gather with our tiny fingers as we sat lisping to ourselves on the grass — the same hips and haws on the autumn hedgerows — the same redbreasts that we used to call "God's birds," because they did no harm to the precious crops. What novelty is worth that sweet monotony where everything is known, and *loved* because it is known? (I, 58; original emphasis)

 have always loved this passage from George Eliot's exquisite novel, *The Mill on the Floss,* and it seems especially relevant at present. A lot of us are having homing instincts. This return to one's earliest home, where "we sat lisping to ourselves on the grass," is about spending time with parents and loved ones during a traumatic period. During the pandemic, we crave the comfort of childhood place. Mine is the setting of my convalescence, which truly began in late summer.

Before I could walk, my mother used to hold me in the cool water of the lake at the end of our road. It was a public access, reached by a long narrow staircase down a bluff, leading straight out onto a weathered grey dock, also long because of the lake's extensive shallows. A firm sandy bottom made the lake ideal for youthful frolicking among schools of minnows who darted in surprised arrows when tiny feet paddled after them.

The fragrant mint and pine lining the shores, the marbling effect of gold sunlight moving through green waves, the startled fish, the firm sand footing, and the lap, lap, lap of waves - these were soothing continuities when we later acquired a wooded plot of land three lots down from the public access dock. For five years, we swam privately and camped out in a tiny wooden cabin with a loft that Dad built, moving freely from cot to shore via a wide straight staircase set into the earth with parental care, across a grassy bank, down six more wooden steps, and onto our own grey dock. Here, we eagerly flung down our towels, gingerly sat for a moment gasping with our toes dangling in the water, before stepping through the water onto the lake floor. There was the beach, with a narrow bit of sand crowded out by mint and reeds, screened on the right from our neighbor by the sweeping boughs of a willow. To the left, we were equally secluded because the house next door was built high on the bluff, with oak and maple clinging to the hillside between us.

We called this part of the lakeshore home when a modest house nudged out the little lofted cabin. In my teen years, a sunfish sailboat lay recumbent on the green bank, staring wistfully out to the waves and the next sail with Dad. A motorboat anchored in waist-level water – my brother's boat, and his daily sport. Wraight water skied in all warm weather but the choppiest. And I, on the wide lawn after a swim, lay basking in the summer sun, reading or dreaming, listening to the breaking waves and the rustle of the purple beech tree. My mother baked indoors and the aroma of pies, bread and cookies eventually coaxed me inside.

Mom tells me that she held me in the lake when I could only crawl in order to help me to feel at home in the water, since I would grow up so near to it. When I was older, all sixth graders in our school district took a boating safety course. Grand Traverse County contains over sixty lakes – the legacy of receding glaciers. In our neighborhood, children earned their independence when parents were satisfied that they would be safe if they ended up in the lake during play.

I was therefore gently schooled in water safety during childhood. Every afternoon from late June through August, Mom took my younger brother and me to the lake, where we would dive from the dock, play "dolphin" and "motorboat" around the pilings, compete to retrieve the pop cans that we threw into the deeper water (filled with sand and duct-taped closed) and somersault clumsily under water. Before and after swim class at Interlochen National Music Camp's hotel beach, we made sandcastles with other staff and faculty children and cannonballed off the raft. With the proud accomplishment of passing junior lifesaving, I had a certificate attesting that I, too, was qualified to keep other swimmers safe.

Thankfully, in our recovery from COVID-19, there's the lake and the childhood in it. Since July, my son, Hollis, and I have been living here in Interlochen, Michigan. We relocated to my childhood neighborhood so that we could spend more time outside in an area of outstanding natural beauty, and where we could form a bubble with my parents so that they could help in looking after Hollis while I continued to heal. We are so very privileged to be in a position where this support is possible. Our plan is that Bruce – my husband and Hollis's dad – will use up all of his remaining vacation days in visiting every few weeks. His job requires him to be in-person, but we feel that he will probably be safe at his workplace. Luckily, his work as a rare book librarian is fairly solitary and keeps him in an area with its own ventilation system.

Retiring to the countryside has been our creative solution to the pandemic. It causes emotional hardship to be apart as a family and we did not make the decision lightly. Hollis and I miss Bruce very much, and only more so as he has just departed yet again. It was, however, the best that we could do and it was certainly better than during the Blitz when, to address another life-threatening situation, British children were billeted to the countryside, but usually without either parent. Hollis has a parent and grandparents present, and his dad regularly visits. Our son loves Michigan where he is used to summering, and I could not have recovered without my parents' assistance. We comforted ourselves that other generations have gotten through terrible times and so would we, and then we counted our many blessings.

The lake is picturesque in its own right, but there's also a kind of synergy with identity that comes from a deep history with a place. Identity largely occurs through our memories, the associations that we have, and our ability to distinguish between the present and the past. However, because the current moment also includes the past (through memories and associations), time layers together. When I am present at this lake, as opposed to any other, recollections flash fleetingly, fugue-like across my consciousness, while an underlying slow ground drones continuously underneath, recalling a more general sense of these waters as always there, before I had language, and for generations. Thus my historical awareness that indigenous people first inhabited this area about 10,300 years ago in the late Paleoindian period also reminds me of a time before white settlers and becomes part of my knowledge of Duck Lake (Douglass 179).

At first, Duck Lake seems a rather prosaic name compared to that bestowed by the Odawa people: Wahbekaness. It sits at the head of the Betsie River, or *la rivière aux Bec-scies* to the French voyageurs who referred to the sawbill ducks, or *bec-scies*. "Duck Lake" makes more sense within this French context. To the original peoples of this land, however, the name Wahbekaness ("Water Lingers") represents a pause before a fifty-four-mile route to Lake Michigan through a network of rivers and lakes. Wahbekanetta ("Water Lingers Again"), the original name for Green Lake on the other side of a quarter mile span of old forest, also refers to this watery progression.

As for Interlochen's name, it acknowledges its situation on the land between the two lakes and later gained additional significance for the interlocking railway tower that arrived along with the logging industry in 1890. In 1889 and 1890, two railway lines were extended from downstate and crossed in the village of Interlochen, just north of Duck and Green Lakes. Establishing a depot in the old-growth forest at the turn of the century made Interlochen easily accessible for fishing and camping holidays, and for children to attend summer camp. The oldest state park in Michigan was founded here in 1917, America's first summer music camp began in 1928, a boarding high school for the fine and performing arts followed in 1962, and a public radio station was established in 1963. The 2010 census indicates that 583 people (142 families) reside in Interlochen: 52.2% White and 43.2% Native American.

Before this settler history, a band of Odawa made their home for centuries in bark lodges and longhouses on the northwestern shore of Wahbekaness. Their cultural emphasis is glimpsed by that which also lingers: their name for the water. This orientation is unsurprising given the Odawa people's famed prowess at building birchbark canoes, their voyages on northern waterways, and the origin of the name Odawa, meaning "trader." In an excellent history of the Little River Band of Ottawa Indians of Manistee and Mason counties (fifteen miles southwest of Interlochen), James M. McClurken reports that the Odawak "facilitated, and at times controlled, trade in the Great Lakes region," not least because no other indigenous peoples paddled canoes across these large freshwater lakes (2). The Odawa people were known as intertribal traders and for exchanging furs with the French as early as 1653, and later for supplying food and canoes to the French (later British) forts located at the Straits of Mackinac between Michigan's upper and lower peninsulas (Wemigwase 10, 19).

Michigan's name, too, indicates the waters. Mi-chi-gum means "monstrous lake," writes Odawa Chief Mack-e-te-be-nessy in 1887 (Blackbird 93). While the name is today shared with the westernmost Great Lake, historian Virgil J. Vogel tells us that to the Anishinaabek, Michigan was "a generic designation for any very large lake and was applied by one or more tribes, in one form or another, to all of the five Great Lakes" (1). According to Professor Margaret Noodin (born Noori), "Minowakiing: The Good Land" is the space around the lakes that was occupied by the Anishinaabek people, a federation comprising the Odawa, Ojibwe and Bodéwadmi tribes.

For the Odawa, the lake and river valleys were life, from their abundant fish to the animals who still have pathways along the water's edge. Here is water, a sustained food supply and pelts from deer, fox, wolf, black bear, rabbit, raccoon, squirrel, skunk, otter, mink, beaver, muskrat and wolverine. The game is especially plentiful because Grand Traverse county is an ecologically diverse area, being the only Michigan county that "lies at the convergence of three major regional landscape divisions" with divergent types of forest and terrain, including outwash plains, dry sand prairie and conifer swamp (Douglass 155). This environmental diversity has been an ongoing feature of the Interlochen area from when the Paleoindian spruce-fir forest supported game such as that found in the Canadian subarctic: "woodland caribou, moose, black bear, snowshoe hare, beaver, muskrat, and porcupine" (Douglass 183). With their winter quarters on Wahbekaness, the local band also found shelter from the direct lake effect snow of northwestern lower Michigan, which is second only to the northern upper peninsula along Lake Superior.

This orientation to the water resonates with the great Chinese philosophical schools of Confucianism, Taoism and Buddhism in which the image of the pond represents the *shen*, or the healthy holistic person (the interdependent psyche, body and spirit). All three Eastern systems aspire to an inner peace that is like the calm pond. To disturb the pond is to muddy it – a cloudiness akin to the strong emotions and overstimulation that can stir the *shen* and lead to disease, according to the renowned acupuncturist, Giovanni Maciocia.

"Water lingers" likewise indicates an ongoing state of calm (it continues to linger). It is the perfect name for the place and the state of being with which a person encounters it. The calmness of the lake with its floor of firm sand is not muddied by ripples on its surface. I find myself attracted to the movement of wind, which the British Romantic poets understood as the breath of God brushing across us and therefore inspiring creativity, hopes, dreams and plans. I listen closely to the wind to learn its messages to me.

അ൞ഠ

I'm sitting at the lake now. It is late August and hazy from the humidity of an early morning thunderstorm. We're at eighty-six degrees Fahrenheit and climbing.

Wahbekaness is a ten-minute walk from our summer cottage. Built by Interlochen summer music camp faculty in 1930, ours is one of the four original cottages of Orchestra Camp Colony. Today, OCC comprises twenty dwellings that nestle in a forest along sandy two-track roads. Most of the cottages have histories attached to the camp, as do many of the owners. Collectively, OCC owns a nature conservancy that stretches almost a third of a mile along the shores of Duck Lake.

The colony also forms the southern tip of a larger, adjacent neighborhood of winterized homes where I grew up. Our present green cottage with blue trim and window boxes filled with pink and red impatiens is a professor's summer writing retreat and a childhood home, for it is situated in the place where I roamed freely with my brother in play.

OCC is private, as is its lake access. We swim in a cove with tall lake grasses on either side providing a living screen, wind-rippled in counterpoint to the faster tempo of the waves: now regular, and then capriciously changing course from the wind or the wake of a passing boat. Blue jays and crickets vie with the motor of an approaching pontoon boat. The loons who nest one cove over remain silent while the murmur of indistinct conversation reveals the presence of unseen companions enjoying a swim and a picnic on the sandbar, just past the southern reeds.

I don't see how a real pond is wholly calm; our lake teems with life, just as a small portion of the *yang* is contained within the *yin* in the *taijitu* (the *yin-yang* symbol). On a sunny day, the ripples glisten diamond-encrusted, but today the pale blue-grey of the sky reflects in the water, interrupted only by the undulating ridgeline of green hills. These shores are variegated, too. A forest of mostly eastern white pine, red pine, white oak and sugar maple, along with hemlock, eastern red cedar, spruce, tamarack, paper birch and bigtooth aspen descends from the hills to water's edge, as if to dangle toes, ankles and knobbly knees. Lazily, they cool roots and dip branches like fingers, offering nutrients to the lake and reciprocally taking news of the waves to the fraternity of bluff-side trees through an interlocking root system.

This lively communication occurs between the still watery-grey of the sky and the mirrored lake, the latter adding textured movement to the reflected color. The tranquility of nature is alive in ways that racing, busy lives do not perceive. Being an active participant with an imagination that fills in the details makes me who I am and roots me further to this lake. It is our quality of thinking and being that determines who we are; it is how we link together the moments of our past, present and enduring selves. Too often this process gets lost as we become subsumed in the pace of modern life with its rush of exciting experiences and cheap commodities.

It is like losing track of the heavy scent of pine in the air. When our family first returns to Michigan from St. Louis, we roll down the windows for the last few miles no matter the temperature, inhaling the coniferous air deep into our lungs. Biologist Diana Beresford-Kroeger researches how the forest's fragrance is actually a chemical-releasing aerosol. The smell emitted by pine, specifically, is "a natural antibiotic," she writes in *The Global Forest*:

> it exerts ... a stimulating effect on the process of breathing itself. It also functions as a mild narcotic. These aerosols have an anesthetic effect on the body, bringing about relaxation ... Other trees do

likewise. In fact the global forests exert an antiviral and antibacterial action on moving air masses, in general. (81)

No wonder I can relax in a pine forest: the trees are designed to assist in rejuvenating and healing. Elsewhere, Beresford-Kroeger reports, "Pines all produce *alpha* and *beta pinenesa*. Research in Japan has found that these aerosols protect the body against cancer by boosting the immune system" ("Green Machines"; see also Li). Soon after arriving in Michigan, we cease consciously to notice the scent of the air, yet it still supports us by filling our lungs with the good medicine of *pinenesa*.

We are more mindful of the lake, which wears different characters, rhythms and hues depending upon hour, season and weather. My family and neighbors are drawn to contemplate it and this absorption calms. The lake is more than a metaphor for holistic health: the action of observing natural beauty assists inner peacefulness. Although Eye Movement Desensitization and Reprocessing, the technique for healing trauma, is usually associated with the horizontal eye movement that occurs during sleep, psychologist Francine Shapiro's inspiration for EMDR came from noticing that being in nature inspires rapid back-and-forth eye movement (9). Simply being physically still and looking at nature's details can promote relaxation and healing.

The lake has been my answer for the depression that I've felt under the weight of illness. When I realized that I must take a medical leave, it became an effort to get up. But I do. I rise, make breakfast for us, encourage Hollis to put on his socks and brush his teeth, and wave him off for a day of distance learning at his grandparents' house, facilitated by my mother. Then I'm alone with a big blank day, reflecting back to me my own depression.

Every morning my thoughts and footsteps wend toward the lake. The peacefulness and mist upon the water will set me up for the whole day: an early calm shared only with an intrepid water skier or two on the far shore. My favorite time has always been the early hours. During summers spent here in my teens and twenties, I would frequently swim upon rising, padding barefoot across the lawn and wincing as I stepped on acorns along the way.

When possible, I still like to walk barefoot, my toes clenching into the sand, establishing a firm hold when I stand still and rock a little on sharp pebbles. Most of today's perambulations occur on paved sidewalks and roads. As one of my creative writing teachers at Interlochen Arts Academy observed, we rarely walk anymore on uneven, unpaved ground. Subsequently, I've made a point of introducing my feet to grass, moss, sand, clay, pebbles and rocks, noticing the minute shifts of balance required to negotiate unmediated earth. It is good to know the naked earth, for her to roughen the balls of my feet into yellow callouses and to require tiny, neglected muscles to shift and balance. It seems especially right that my body should be viscerally relating to nature at present, rather than only coming into contact through rubberized soles (souls) on ground mechanically smoothed and then hidden under concrete, like colonization.

The journey to the lake begins outside our screen door with the sandy two-track road that runs along the top of the conservancy bluff. The middle hump in Orchestra Drive sprouts just enough grass for a suggestion of green to emerge now and then from the brindled shadows cast on the road by a canopy of leafy branches. Horizontally, tree roots rib sections of the drive before the little dip to a leaf-covered loamy valley. To either side of the dirt road, the woodland floor shifts between ubiquitous hillocks of moss and last season's leaves, russet pine needles, sandy ant hills, feathery ferns and the occasional group of mushrooms – large free-standing toadstools, frilly ballerina-skirted stumps, and the red caps with white spots of children's tea sets and fairy tales.

Four cottages blink sleepily to my left: olive with white trim; vanilla-bean brown with a long screened porch and a wee fairy garden for the grandchildren; milky cappuccino with skylights; and a log cabin with a substantial stone chimney. The last two remain boarded up this summer, unoccupied because of the pandemic. Their owners dream of summer in Michigan while their cottages, resolute if forlorn, wait patiently for their people to return as their boarded windows drowse on. Lights blink on in the olive cottage, however, as coffee percolates, pancake batter sizzles and Frankie the dog ratta-tat-tats his black and white tail in happy anticipation of his first walk.

Above, slender grey trees rise straight, their trunks punctuating the enveloping leaves and pine boughs. They look like sound to me, as if the treads in Edward Burne-Jones's splendid painting of *The Golden Stairs* had tilted sideways and elongated in their reach toward heaven. In the picture, a bevy of bare-footed young ladies in classical gowns hold musical instruments and descend an interior staircase. At the top of the canvas is a patch of exposed blue sky. Art scholars consider the lineation and repetition in this painting to be a visual rendition of metrical sound, as suggested by the musical instruments in the picture. Like the punch cards of player piano sheet music or the raised surfaces of music box paper, visible and tactile patterns can be transformed to sound. In the forest, you can hear sonority if you listen closely to a natural Jacob's ladder, reaching suggestively up. I see rhythmic sound in the patterns of long grey trunks extending from each unique earth-anchor toward the shared heavens, just as I hear the hollow tap of the red-headed woodpecker between the squawk of blue jays.

On high, the sky dapples in large patches of blue and white across which the highest leaves distinguish themselves as individuated from the expanse of variegated green – a fluttering of excited motion and a rustling that endows the breeze with sound and makes visible the wind. Their parent trees' silver trunks, immobile in the slight whisper of air, line up with others in uneven punctuation. The spaces between these vertical ribbons of lichen-spotted grey-green stand in counterpoint to the giddy flurry of the canopy.

So majestically alive, the oxygen-producing trees and the lichen interact with each other and with other trees through their roots, the breeze, and the birds and squirrels alighting on their branches. These trees, glorious to the eye, indicate "atmospheric health" through the presence of their lichens, for "lichens will not grow in polluted air," writes Beresford-Kroeger in *To Speak for the Trees* (167).

Perhaps this mutually supportive community can serve as an example for a healthier way of being. In the West, our subjective sense of self usually aligns with second-order surveillance, where we make sense of ourselves through a process of feeling watched. The French philosopher, Michel Foucault, explains in his seminal study, *Discipline and Punish: The Birth of the Prison* (1975), how social control through a displayed, garish warning (the gallows) shifted at the turn of the nineteenth century to architectural structures that utilized the sense of being watched to organize workers in factories, limit theft in department stores and to control incarcerated persons. The first two were designed with an open ground floor and a balcony from which managers could observe factory hands and customers. The last is exemplified by the Panopticon: a prison distinguished by a central watchtower inside an encircling block of cells, each backlit so that guards could watch inmates without the prisoners knowing when they were being surveyed. Ever since Freud's talking cure, therapists have also watched while a patient reflects aloud and identifies areas for self-correction. School children similarly learn to construct a sense of identity through hierarchical grading systems that offer "norms" against which individuals measure themselves in order to improve.

In contrast, as I walk within a rich ecosystem, feet balancing on uneven ground, my walking is respectful and interactive because of a peaceful contemplation. Rather than seeking to control or feeling manipulated through the gaze, the emphasis shifts to a search for healing and for a better knowledge of self through simply observing the natural world. It is not about trying to excel or compete.

As I amble along the two-track, this fluid consciousness shifts again - suddenly - to the feet in order safely to navigate first a short, steep path and then an uneven rustic set of stairs that descend the bluff. The treads are created by laying down wooden four-by-fours and filling in the top with soil. Following the landscape, the steps range in shape from rectangles to triangular wedges, thus enabling a curve. The handrail, likewise, is of the land, made of three slim tree trunks with knots like phantom limbs. With varied heights and widths, these are not stairs for the infirm. Nor is the subsequent boardwalk, tilting like a gigantic, undulating keyboard over a muddy bog. The boards of various hue attest to the annual spring triage when the community works together to replace rotted boards. "Mosquito Swamp" we have dubbed this stretch. With dull thudding feet, I hasten over the wetlands in order to escape a blood-thirsty bombardment.

A winding path follows, treated with cedar chips and gracefully lined with white birch. It passes an overgrown picnic area with one lone weathered picnic table, unevenly polka dotted with the blue juice of dropping berries. Then ... the lake emerges. One more mindful task remains and that is a careful maneuvering of the worn dock so as not to drop the plastic Adirondack chair legs through the chinks or to scrape a splinter into my heel.

Because it requires attention to the way itself, this uneven ambulatory approach to the lake is preparation for being present: here, now, fully conscious. There is direction, purpose and focus on the moment. This path leads to the lake. That intention motivates the walk and anticipates the pleasure of arrival. More importantly, this prelude to Wahbekaness - filled with variegated motion and awareness - creates a frame of mind for lingering with a greater awareness of what comes next: the quality of stillness in contemplating the water.

The path, then, leads to myself.

With tea balanced on the wide arm of the green chair, peace gradually dispels the depression. There is strength and sympathy in the splendor of these northern woods and waters. The synergy of identity with a multi-leveled history in a place, furthermore, takes healing to a level that the English school of Lake Poets understood in the late eighteenth and early nineteenth centuries. As a professor of nineteenth-century British literature, this connection seems natural to me, especially since the Lake District in northwestern England reminds me of my Michigan home. Forested lakes like Windermere and Coniston Water quenched my homesickness when I first encountered them at twenty-one, while their mountainous terrain and slate stone cottages added an agreeable note of difference that I still relish.

William Wordsworth's masterful poem, "Tintern Abbey," seems especially relevant to my consideration of the layering of times within an evocative place:

> Five years have past; five summers with the length
> Of five long winters! and again I hear
> These waters,
>
> ...
>
>   Though absent long,
> These forms of beauty have not been to me,
> As is a landscape to a blind man's eye:
> But oft, in lonely rooms, and 'mid the din
> Of towns and cities, I have owed to them,
> In hours of weariness, sensations sweet,
>
> ...
>
> With tranquil restoration:—feelings too
> Of unremembered pleasure: such, perhaps,
> As may have had no trivial influence
> On that best portion of a good man's life; (1–3, 23–8, 31–34)

Wordsworth's experience unites the value that he found in a place five years previously with the intervening years, when that place offered "tranquil restoration" for the "din" and pace of industrial, urban life. The poem goes on to reveal that his sister accompanies him in the present visit. William anticipates that Dorothy will similarly take away from the scene a comfort for her future. Contemplating the Wye river in England thus unites past, present and future, providing an ongoing sense of center that Wordsworth understands to have great influence on "that best portion of a good [person's] life."

Such concepts of how one might find joy through encounters with nature and "emotion recollected in tranquillity" (Preface 183) became Wordsworth's literary theory, philosophy and the substance of his poems. These ideas profoundly influenced his contemporaries and those who followed, including John Stuart Mill. This Victorian philosopher had been nursed on Jeremy Bentham's Utilitarianism: a non-religious and highly influential attempt in late eighteenth- and early nineteenth-century Britain to provide a social structure that systematized ethics. (Bentham was also responsible for the idea of the Panopticon.) Mill was not alone in finding Utilitarianism to be problematic. Charles Dickens opened his novel, *Hard Times* with a pointed criticism of Utilitarianism: "NOW, what I want is, Facts," Thomas Gradgrind demands of schoolchildren. "Facts alone are wanted in life" (47). Such an orientation fares badly in the novel from 1854, as it did in real lives.

As a young man, depressed because of his own Utilitarian upbringing, Mill found in poetry a wellspring for individual happiness and an alternative social model. "What made Wordsworth's poems a medicine for my state of mind," wrote Mill, was that,

> In them I seemed to draw from a source of inward joy, of sympathetic and imaginative pleasure, which could be shared in by all human beings; ... I needed to be made to feel that there was real, permanent happiness in tranquil contemplation. Wordsworth taught me this, not only without turning away from, but with a greatly increased interest in the common feelings and common destiny of human beings. (104)

Sympathy for others could hold communities together.

"Tintern Abbey" specifically addresses how individual contemplation could lead to a happiness that was inherently social, for the poet's joy increases as he witnesses Dorothy's pleasure: "in thy voice I catch / The language of my former heart, and read / My former pleasures in the shooting lights / Of thy wild eyes" (117–20). This passage communicates a wisdom in terms that traditional Eastern medicine recognizes: the eyes are the window to the soul and the spirit (*shen*) is linked to the element of fire. Wordsworth reads in Dorothy's heart-voice and shooting-light-eyes their shared self, which emerges from contemplating natural beauty. The poet's thankfulness for experiencing again the freshness of the scene through his sister's joyful observations reveals a different motivation than watching for the sake of controlling behavior. As my student Heather Bozant Witcher explored in her doctoral research on the legacy of Adam Smith's ideas in nineteenth-century Britain, this sort of experience was understood to form a bond through mutual aesthetic and spiritual joy.

This idea of sympathetic surveillance was foundational for Mill's healing process, too. As a reader, he observed Wordsworth's contemplations in poetry, including the prayer with which "Tintern Abbey" concludes: "If solitude, or fear, or pain or grief, /Should be thy portion, with what healing thoughts / Of tender joy wilt thou remember me, / And these my exhortations!" (144–7). Mill tells us in his *Autobiography* that he learns a similar "permanent happiness in tranquil contemplation." While the specific future is unknown in the cited passage ("if" begins a list of possible difficulties), Wordsworth is certain that Dorothy will remember him and the fervency of his appeal (marked by an exclamation point). Because part of Wordsworth's composition process was to read Dorothy's journals in order to remind himself of the immediacy of shared experiences, perhaps he can confidently make this assertion (he writes the poem from the future).

In Wordsworth's ardent hope that this present moment of contemplation will forever aid his sister, there is much that is similar to the stance of those who followed, from the New England Transcendentalists to our own family situation. As Henry David Thoreau sought in 1847 to live more simply away from neighbors in Massachusetts in a cabin overlooking a glacial pond and then to share what he learned in *Walden; Or, Life in the Woods,* so has our family escaped the novel coronavirus. I seek a healthier life as part of the healing from a virus and the strains of modernity itself, in a cottage above our own glacial lake in Michigan. Unlike Thoreau, however, my return to Michigan is a return to beginnings.

My present story seeks to understand others and myself in relation to past, present and future communities. Even this approach is a reclamation of an ongoing self that got lost in the scurry of recent years. From childhood, I would feel my connection to this shoreline as if I were one of the Anishinaabek. This is not an act of appropriation, but rather a child's admiration combined with my mother's teachings to be at one with the earth and water. My dreams were of travelling far through virgin pines with deep respect for all creatures found there. I'd see the birch trees leaning over the water and, along with appreciating the living trees, I was aware of the birch as one my mother's favorite trees. I would also associate the curled white bark strewn on the bank with Odawa canoes made for long-distance travel. People have histories of things that interest them and that contribute to the building of associative links that underpin thought processes and senses of identity.

As the next weeks unfolded, radiant joy and healing emerged from simultaneously recovering and developing an even deeper relationship with the earth and other sentient beings, whether five-fingered, four-footed, feathered or finned. I began fully to relax in the week after Labor Day. Bruce had been for a visit and it felt so good to be together as a full family. Hollis always runs to greet him when Bruce first pulls into the driveway. Our son blossoms during his dad's visit and we all breathe more deeply together, here in the woods. I find it exponentially more difficult to say good-bye to Bruce each time that he returns to St. Louis after a visit with us in Michigan, where together we find "tranquil restoration."

2 | The Arrow Tree

HEN I was small, my mother, brother and I would walk from our red front door past a white house to the corner of two paved streets, one running parallel to the lakeshore of Wahbekaness and the other leading perpendicularly toward Wahbekanetta. She would lift me up and set me on an oak tree bent by the Odawa into an arrow, pointing to our lake. It had a little bump on the horizontal bit, making a perfect saddle. A nub on the other side of the trunk from my perch proved it to be a manipulated tree; this knob indicated where it had been tied as a sapling in order to redirect its growth. White oaks like this live an average of three hundred years and can mature to around six hundred. As a young tree, it had been shaped so that its trunk grew first straight up from the ground, then bent at a right angle, and then reached for the heavens with branches like elongated fingers.

This tree connects my infant experiences with my adult life. In my walks through the years, I always check to make sure that it remains, a link among the generative care of mother and child, and also those who shaped it into a marker. Artist Ladislav R. Hanka's discussions with tribal elders of the Little Traverse Bay Bands of Odawa Indians underpin his recognition that trees bent by the Odawak are cultural as well as trail markers, indicating "mostly ... ancient trail-ways," but also "an auspicious crossroads" or a cemetery. In the narrative that accompanies an exhibit of his striking etchings, Hanka calls marker trees "a living link to that earlier time, before the long-reigning balance was tipped. They are icons and carry the trace of a biological memory accreted slowly with each year's ring of growth. They are real; you can touch them; they are alive; they are a worthy subject for art." The Interlochen bent tree's memory includes my gentle fingers, decades after the touch of the hands that shaped it. When I lay my palm on it now, perhaps it can feel my own tough survival of COVID-19. Like this crooked tree, I am "fierce in a way that demands recognition – reflecting the adversity they [and I] have survived" – from lightning to road crews (Hanka).

We have more in common, for my forename means "a green leaf or bough," from the Greek *phylon*. Before being associated with the pastoral shepherdess in Renaissance madrigals like John Farmer's "Fair Phyllis I Saw Sitting All Alone" (1599), Phyllis was immortalized respectively by Herodotus and Chaucer in a myth of metamorphosis. Transformed into an almond tree when she hanged herself in the belief that her lover Demophoon had abandoned her, Phyllis reemerges in Edward Burne-Jones's painting of 1870 to reclaim Demophoon.

My name holds a transformation for me, too, for I share it with my maternal grandmother. She died two years before my birth. Love, honor, loss and lineage all cohabitate in this name. With this realization of matrilineal links, I wonder what is passed down, too, through the chemical transferences during pregnancy. For female fetuses have hundreds of thousands of eggs in their ovaries by the fourth month of development. Thus, when she was pregnant with my mother, Grandma Phyllis also carried the seeds of me and my brother in a sense. What cultural memories have entered our biology through grandmothers holding daughters along with grandchildren?

At a family funeral a few years ago, I spoke with people who remember my grandmother. "What was she like?" I asked one woman who had been her student and also boarded with the family during her senior year in high school.

She didn't miss a beat. "You are her."

I gaped. That was unexpected.

Apparently, how I hold myself, speak and interact – these attributes are shared along with our name – as well as our interests and even ambitions. My grandmother, rather unusually for a woman in the early twentieth century, had an MA in English literature. Before her premature death in 1966, she was formulating a plan to return for her doctorate. In our family, this predilection for higher education in English literature seems to have passed through the female line and I have fulfilled my grandmother's dreams.

What does biological lineage mean for my own son who came to us through adoption? Because our son mirrors our facial expressions, he carries something in him of the emotional chemicals released by our joys and our stresses, too. But, as he would proudly tell you, he is rich in ancestry by having two families: one genetic (whose identity remains hidden because of Chinese policies) and the other formed with us through culture, lived memories and daily nurturing.

The solid tree upon which my mother set me pointed with its bent trunk to the lake and, with its green boughs ("Phyllis"), to matrilineal lineage. It spoke of mother's care: of playful walks and making up songs to sing together, of learning to pay attention to the feel of rough bark and the look of light streaming through the leaves. Mom, too, found home in a tree, although in her case it was the countless hours spent climbing the purple beech in front of her childhood home. On her thirty-fifth birthday, my parents planted another purple beech outside the living room window of our house on Duck Lake. Mom found peace and her childhood in the wind rustling its leaves, and she glimpsed the future in her grandson hanging from its branches. Hollis, too, would prefer to be reading in a tree rather than standing on the ground.

Trail marker trees are like people who have depths that are not immediately apparent. Any passerby with knowledge of indigenous ways can read the significance of the bent tree in the woods. However, because my mother playfully sat me on it while simultaneously schooling me to pay attention to the look, feel, sound and smell of individual trees, it became part of my identity, heritage, manner of perception and subjective sense of self. While I climbed white pines in later years to play and read among their branches, this oak of which I made a steed continued to be *my* oak, not in the sense of ownership, but rather as a point of view. Because my family do not own the little wooded plot on which it grows, the arrow tree is all the dearer to me. I cannot protect it except by caring about it. I am concerned for its survival.

This tree, moreover, may not point in the direction that you think. The crooked oak to which my childish hands clung and patted seems to signpost the path between the two lakes. Frequently, kinked trees are simply "directional markers," according to John Bailey, a citizen of the Grand River Bands of Ottawa Indians in Michigan. "They tell you, 'We are heading north or headed west'" (cited in Puit). Certainly, this tree aligns with the east/west axis as well as the shortest portage between Wahbekaness and Wahbekanetta. However, when I discovered another such arrow tree which points south, roughly in the direction of my youthful saddle tree, I needed to reconfigure my mental map of the trail system. This newfound marker tree is preserved within a lawn, pointing parallel to the dirt road on which the house sits. Also a white oak, this arboreal signpost is about the same size and shape as the one from my childhood. Discovering this tree changed my conceptualization from a pathway between the two lakes to a trail through the trees, roughly along the Wahbekanetta shoreline. Thus the original arrow tree also indicates the woods through which you must pass alongside the water.

It takes observation and knowledge of the larger forest to see these details. When I mentioned the new trail marker to my mother, she expressed interest. She had not seen this tree in the lawn, but she told me of several along the lakeshore within the state park. In a sense, many of these last have become ghost trees. We know of one extant white oak that continues to point south from a high bank along the shore. The rest have since fallen naturally or, if diseased, have been removed by the rangers. As trees within a first-growth forest, we can be confident that they are, or were, older than the directional trees in our neighborhood, which were probably bent during the second-growth reforestation at the turn of the twentieth century in order to blaze the trail afresh. In that sense, the tree of my youth was both itself and also the physical memory of earlier navigational trees. The arrow tree is a cultural sign of an intent to remain and to flourish again, despite the devastation of lumbering and forest fire.

Linked together, it would seem that there were two paths. The water route appears to travel from the winter camp just north of the current state park, south along the state park shoreline and then turn inland for portage across the short spur of land between the two lakes that gives Interlochen its name. Geographically, this route makes sense as the quickest way to travel the network of waterways leading to Lake Michigan (it bypasses the Little Betsie River, and the portage point on the Wahbekanetta shore is closer to the outlet of the Betsie River proper). Alternatively, the southern-pointing lawn tree indicates a land route through the forest, possibly an offshoot of the well-travelled Traverse City to Cadillac trail, established by at least the thirteenth century and now easily retraced by driving most of the fifty-five miles (see Ettawagheshik; Crick).

Upon reflection, as the oak tree means more than it first appears, my topic is more than that I once sat upon a tree. To the Odawa, the trail tree signified movement and navigation. It was also a testimony to the intent of the trail maker who wished to make the original way a frequented and continual path. Thus the tree communicated with future travelers. Existing in line with current roads, it reveals that we still follow these ancient ways. Eric Hemenway, Director of the Department of Reparation, Archives and Records for the Little Traverse Bay Bands of Ottawa Indians, reveals that more frequented paved roads also follow Indian trails, from Michigan Scenic Route 31 near us to large Interstates like 75 and 96 (Driscoll). The land is marked with the presence of the people who were, are and will be.

The arrow tree offers direction in my life, too. It points me along productive paths of knowing self through my forested surroundings. As I discover ancient trailways and a rich biodiversity in the woods, so can this time of healing be about perspective and fresh (in)sight. Thus new growth sometimes arises from what at first feels destructive.

෴

This summer in Michigan, we three family members strung brightly colored hammocks between trees like multicolored ribbons of navy, forest green, baby blue and orange. We sprayed on mosquito repellent and spent hours reading, napping or simply observing the surrounding world. Gazing up, I discovered the lively community that existed above: birds sitting on branches and squirrels daringly leaping from veritable twigs, swaying as they caught a skinny branch on the next tree. Chattering to one another, they splayed vertically on the trunk, whisking their tails in warning of my presence or that of the cat. To all sides, there was the green of pines and deciduous trees, a rich foliage with a small vee through which the lake could be glimpsed below the bluff.

Under us stretched the root system with which the trees communicate. Botanist Robin Wall Kimmerer explains in her fascinating book, *Braiding Sweetgrass*:

> The trees in a forest are often interconnected by subterranean networks of mycorrhizal, fungal strands that inhabit tree roots. The mycorrhizal symbiosis enables the fungi to forage for mineral nutrients in the soil and deliver them to the tree in exchange for carbohydrates. The mycorrhizae may form fungal bridges between individual trees, so that all the trees in a forest are connected. These fungal networks appear to redistribute the wealth of carbohydrates from tree to tree ... They weave a web of reciprocity, of giving and taking. In this way, the trees all act as one because the fungi have connected them. Through unity, survival. (20)

"All flourishing is mutual," Kimmerer concludes (20).

For human beings, the medicinal qualities of heart-healing beauty can be part of this prosperity. While rocked in my green and blue nylon hammock, I feel a larger cradling, swaddled in a woods that comforts, talks and sways on all sides, rich with the life of giant trees, the verdant flora of ground cover, and the singing, clucking wildlife, all interdependent and giving bountifully to one another.

This morning, I awoke not to the loon's call as usual in the warm months, but rather to the honking of Canada geese migrating south. Here is another arrow. The community flies in wedge formation high over the blazes of red maple below, each bird taking a turn as leader (wind breaker) for the others.

It is a week of unusually warm September weather before the autumnal chill descends. From the hammock refuge, the tops of trees seem to set the sky on fire, fanned by pine-needle screens of green. It is almost dangerous deep in the woods now because fall is more than a season: it is a verb. Acorns drop from trees with such force that a bike helmet might be advisable. The splats of these brown-capped seeds picks up on a windy day like this when the blowing canopy punctuates its rustlings, shaking off acorns like a wet dog after a swim. Soon leaves will follow the downward descent of the protein-rich acorns to cover the emerald moss with a natural fertilizer laden with carbon, nitrogen and phosphorus.

I love waking to the greenery peeking in from every window in the morning and, as twilight descends, watching the silhouette of the darkening leaves through the skylight. This type of observation is part of the healing of forest bathing (*Shinrin-yoku*), a Japanese practice of being still in the woods. Researchers in Japan have discovered that the benefits of "taking in the forest atmosphere" occur through inhaling "beneficial bacteria, plant-derived essential oils, and negatively-charged ions" (Tsunetsugu; Tatera). The myriad health benefits have been gathered by a team working at University of East Anglia to compile evidence from over 140 studies and twenty countries that show reduction in "diastolic blood pressure, heart rate and stress" as well as "the risk of type II diabetes, cardiovascular disease, premature death, and preterm birth." Sleep duration is increased and "exposure to a diverse variety of bacteria present in natural areas may also have benefits for the immune system and reduce inflammation" (University of East Anglia). Deep immersion in forest-living is certainly assisting me. These scientific studies help me to trust my instincts about what I am already finding to be healthy.

Sometimes navigating what is happening to me feels like the darkness of a forest at night. Without a flashlight during summer evenings, I've sometimes stumbled off the path and run into great, black trees on my way to and from Laurie's firepit next door. Here, we sit socially distanced in wooden Adirondack chairs to roast hotdogs and make s'mores over the embers of cheerful campfires. The unexpected whip in the face of branches is not unlike the sudden panic that I've felt at contemplating a life of chronic illness and latent symptoms. The latter anxiety is so extreme that it usually brings an onset of nausea in its wake. Would I never hike, run or cycle again?

Navigating a dark forest recalls the opening of Dante Alighieri's *La Divina Commedia*, translated here by Robert and Jean Hollander:

> Midway in the journey of our life
> I came to myself in a dark wood,
> for the straight way was lost. (3)

> *Nel mezzo del cammin di nostra vita / mi ritrovai per una selva oscura, / ché la diritta via era smarrita.* (2)

Dante enters limbo during a midlife crisis and then traverses the inferno, purgatory and heaven. He thereby discovers his way instead of wandering darkly. How do people with long COVID similarly find their path when "the straight way [is] lost"?

My "straight way" had been to respond to the aftermath of the acute phase of COVID-19 by attempting to resume my demanding life as I would after any other illness. However, in a situation where all my energy had been required simply to survive, turning back to life as I had known it was impossible. I had exhausted my energetic reserves and had not yet replenished them. My path lay through the dark woods – the unknown – not through a resumption of normal work life.

Of course, if you give your eyes time to adjust to the night, the moon and the starry sky can offer quite a lot of illumination, even in the forest. On a clear night, the lake shines so brightly as the moon rises over the far shore that the water glimmers through the trees. This beckoning light reminds me of the Anishinaabek's Grandmother Moon who, as the first mother of humanity, ascended the sky to remind her descendants of her presence and continual guidance (Johnston 26). Healing only began when I gave myself permission to adjust to what at first seemed dark, or to find a way to shift expectations of myself. During this rebalancing time, grandparents and children may come together in myriad ways for mutual benefit as teachers and fulfillers of dreams.

Simply resting and watching the northern woods and waters helped me to understand the self beneath my working identity. My acupuncturist, Abigail, tells me that traditional Chinese medicine understands this situation as needing to vanquish the non-self that is still occupying my system in order to reach self, or an integrated health on all levels. The non-self comprises the ongoing COVID symptoms, but another non-self is also in occupation. When I stop to ask myself what is causing me to feel ill in my daily, modern life (beyond CV-19 and its sequelae), I know the answer immediately: I am overworking.

I love my occupation and feel fortunate to hold the position that I do. Life as a university professor certainly has its privileges, but it is far from the cushy job that most people assume it to be. I speak here of workload; I have not experienced the additional burden of discrimination because of race, sexual orientation, disability, religion or socioeconomic status. I have always worked at least eighty hours a week year-round and have not taken my full annual holiday. Beyond devising and offering new classes at the undergraduate and graduate levels, and being available as an advisor, I participate in graduate examinations and direct master's and doctoral research. The last are book-length projects that require multiple revisions of each chapter. On an ongoing basis, I undertake my own research and publications, which informs my teaching and my activities outside the ivory tower. I write and present for the media, offer several conference papers and invited lectures annually, write grant proposals (some number over a hundred pages each), serve as a blind (unpaid) reviewer for publications and international fellowship competitions, support multiple students and colleagues with detailed recommendation letters, and evaluate large tenure and promotion portfolios, each comprising multiple publications (books and articles). Then there is the administrative service to the department, college, university and profession, including serving on multiple committees and boards. What I have just outlined is only a part of my workload, for I also currently direct the Center for Digital Humanities at our university.

Right now, however, I am an academic finding herself not in the university, but rather through the living wood, where darkness and light coexist. Thought of in terms of the pioneers who sought to define a specifically American culture after the US War of Independence, we might think of the symbols of the axe and the arrow tree as the twin faces of a coexistence: one builds modern society while the other points to nature. When I was a student at Cambridge, one of the great literary professors, Tony Tanner, spoke in our seminars about the symbolism of the axe in American frontier literature. The handle was made of wood and the axe also cut down wood. Settlers both revered and destroyed the old-growth forest in order to support cultivation, using a tool made from the tree itself. In contrast, the solid oak on which my mother placed me in her wisdom and love is an antidote to the axe. It is the living wood that survives or emerges after deforestation, and an emblem of the peaceful interaction between humanity and the natural world.

There is no doubt that current American culture is especially driven, but how is overwork like an axe? The effects of stress on physical health are not unlike the ravages to the ecosystem brought about by cutting primary forests. Around the time that my grandparents were born, heavy logging in Interlochen supplied the Wylie Cooperage Company with the materials to make barrels. By 1897, the Traverse City newspaper reported of this "Thriving Center" that the company cut 4,000,000 feet of logs to make "60,000 hoops and 30,000 staves." It devastates me to think of those majestic 120-foot pines being cut for thin wooden hoops and slats. Old photos show the result: a ravaged earth with expanses of stumps like wastelands. Loggers left debris ("slash") as they hurriedly left exhausted cut sites which subsequently caused terrible forest fires.

The damage to natural environments is more readily comprehended today than the consequences of overwork and stress to our health. Yet as I turn to in Chapter 15, this state of things reveals an ideology of work, rather than the way that things have to be. During the height of the logging industry, North American and British societies were more concerned with limiting working hours and supporting initiatives to cultivate the whole person than they were with protecting natural resources. At the time, the earth's bounty seemed unending.

In a similar way, a healthy person has seemingly boundless sources of energy and strength because he or she has reserves from which to draw. It took long COVID for me to realize just how much effort goes into the critical thinking where I had been used to locating "self." In the right balance, I find great inner peace when I am engaged in scholarship. However, it becomes "non-self" – a pathogen – when it shifts to overwork. This idea of balance holds true for any activity. While the West generally applauds extreme achievements like running marathons and writing academic monographs, in traditional Eastern medicine, intense activity is understood as overdoing it. Rather than being the height of fitness, any excess overtaxes a person's *qi* and depletes *yang*. I only realized that "non-self" is a pathogen, however, when I was so weak as to feel acutely when I was overdoing anything. Overworking, overthinking and over-exercising all manifested as bodily illness.

Equilibrium can be attained again through balancing my activities: by enrichening my sense of who I am and therefore how I spend my time. When I sit on the lakeshore and watch the golden reeds bend with the wind or lie in the hammock and observe the treetops interlacing their leaves as they, too, stir with the breeze, I connect with the world more broadly. In this sense, I am not defined so fully by my job. Even if work is a vocation, it only comprises a portion of the wider landscape of self.

Trees often symbolize the way in which people identify with the land. Virginia Woolf, for example, features an oak at the center of *Orlando: A Biography*. In this novel from 1928, the time-travelling protagonist finds in the great English oak a symbol of her landed estate and the world itself:

> The ferny path led ... higher to the oak tree, which stood on the top. The tree had grown bigger, sturdier, and more knotted since she had known it, somewhere about the year 1558, but it was still in the prime of life ... Flinging herself on the ground, she felt the bones of the tree running out like ribs from a spine this way and that beneath her. She liked to think that she was riding the back of the world ... As she flung herself down a little square book bound in red cloth fell from the breast of her leather jacket – her poem "The Oak Tree". "I should have brought a trowel," she reflected. (224)

This oak, the spine of the world, inspires Orlando's great literary endeavor, begun as a child and written over the course of 300 years, roughly corresponding to the English oak's lifespan. Her poetic tribute is a constant companion, reflecting in its leaves the stains of sea, travel and blood. Burying the manuscript at the base of the referent tree was to have been a symbolic gesture, "'a return to the land of what the land has given me,'" Orlando was going to say in praise (225). Finally, Orlando's focus is not so much on the poem as on the tree itself as inspirational.

My crooked tree is also inherently more than its bent trunk or the signification with which human hands and eyes endow it. What a gorgeous, multi-hued trunk, covered in ripple-rough grey bark that hides sap flowing through the variegated growth rings of its core. It has a history, some of which I know and more of which I might surmise. I expect that the hands that shaped it into a trail marker did so prayerfully, with an offering of tobacco accompanying a request to the tree that it agree to be shaped. Tobacco signals the greatest respect. It is and was "a gift of the spirit" and "a tangible, sensible, substance [that] represented the union between man and his God; and prefigured man's own final destiny" (Johnston 43). The tree was probably understood to communicate agreement to the signposting request. Thankfully, it continues to grow and exist in symbiosis with us, although I suspect that most people today pass it without pausing to notice it at the crossroads, much less to reflect on its shape.

The trail blazer seems to point beyond itself to the lake and the forest, but it also carries another less obvious meaning. Beneath its modest gesture away from itself is the inherent value of the tree. The shape distracts us from thinking about the oak as more than a signpost.

The arrow tree is in this way like those of us who are finding our way through a mystery illness. Its essence remains strong and healthy, like any other tree in the forest. But it is a special tree. The Odawa made distinctive trees into much more than geographical points of navigation, including those that are naturally bent. The most famous example of this in northwestern lower Michigan was a large pine "whose top was very crooked, almost hook-like," growing out of a bluff near present-day Good Hart. This unusual tree was a point by which to steer for bands arriving each summer by canoe. Here they would find the village of Waganakising, "meaning the crooked top of the tree" (Blackbird 10), or *L'Arbre Croche* to the French. The tree is no longer there, but the self-referent of their descendants is Waganakising Odawak (federally reaffirmed as the Little Traverse Bay Bands of Odawa Indians). Thus a crooked tree is simultaneously itself with running sap, leafing branches and roots in mycorrhizal communication with the forest and the lake, and it also has become a marker for a community and its individuals even after it was needlessly cut at the turn of the nineteenth century (Tanner 19). Perhaps it signals the importance to the Odawak, too, of self identity as inherently relational with land and extended family, clan and tribal band.

While a crooked tree signifies the Odawak people of Good Hart, for me, trees with altered growth suggest personal resilience. Other eyes may first see little beyond the unusual shape of a navigational tree; what I contemplate, however, is a special and unusually hearty being, with a trunk like a muscle flexing to support the handsome curvatures rising above.

With its arm extended high to the sky, its back agreeably hunched into a saddle for a child, and its roots elongating through the earth toward the lake, what this grand oak finally requires and elicits is respect. I approached it again this summer with a glad greeting and a troubled question: How *do* I become fully whole? In her TEDx talk, Margaret Noodin discusses the hieroglyphic found in Michigan of a hunter with an arrow notched on the bow. Tribal elders told her that rather than hunger, the picture communicated going into the future in ways that we cannot always predict. Where is the future, I wonder, to which an arrow tree points? It indicates a path in the woods, but also our step-by-step journey into the unknown. Thankfully, the wild world is interconnected, Noodin observes, with networks of relationships. My mother taught me this, too, and that nature will help us.

Through my family, I learned to go to the forest and lake when I needed to release grief and anger. At one point, when I was very young, feeling grumpy, and probably annoying adult family members, my Great Aunt Millie took me out on our cross country skis into the neighboring state park. We skied into the woods where we encountered several old-growth hemlocks with their boughs bent deep under several inches of snow. She lined me up underneath and released the weighted branches. They sprang up, sprinkling me with snow to my great delight. Our laughter magically changed churlishness into ringing forest tones while also disburdening the trees. Every time I pass these trees, I think of Millie who kindly taught me how to release my mood with the help of some trees and thereby to return smiling to my family.

Now, I seek peace in a cabin enveloped and lulled by the trees. It upsets me to be ill and for so long, and I am releasing these feelings into this forest. It helps that I am here in my favorite season for the first time in decades. I adore the trees' brilliant foliage, to which human eyes turn with wonder as neon red and orange foliage flares high into the sky. Their preciousness is increased because of the short time before they will fall. And leave.

It is fitting that autumn is conceived as a time of passing on in many cultures: North America's Halloween, Mexico's *Día de Muertos*, Christianity's All Souls Day, and American Indian Ghost Suppers, such as the Odawa tradition of Jiibay Wiikongewin Gichitwaawin, meant to maintain a connection with ancestors. Chinese beliefs align. In traditional Chinese medicine, where the health of the mind/body is conceived as unified (not dual, as in the West), the spirit is understood as the totality of the energy of the heart, kidney, spleen, lungs and liver, each of which have mental and emotional qualities. Disturbances in the psyche can affect bodily health.

Because the *shen* is the totality of this vascular system and also the name of the heart element, the concept of *shen* means much more than the rough translation it is usually given as "spirit." Giovanni Maciocia, the author of influential acupuncture textbooks, explains that the word "*shen*" is composed of two pictograms. The first contains elements indicating the spiritual, the sacrificial altar and a spirit tablet where the dead were understood to gather. Thus one part of the *shen* points to the indestructible, ethereal qualities of the soul. The second pictogram comprises the quality of reaching out calmly to relate and to connect with other people. In the video interviews from 2019 that extend his influential book, *The Psyche in Chinese Medicine: Treatment of Emotional and Mental Disharmonies with Acupuncture and Chinese Herbs* (2009), Maciocia discusses how Chinese culture, both ancient and modern, understands *gui* as a balanced, healthy movement between generations.

Ancestral attachments are becoming more important to me as my parents age and as I have been afraid during our illness for the well-being of my child and myself. It is psychologically healthy to feel connected to our loved ones, whether alive or departed. Yet I've lost part of that foundation; I've been out of touch with my ancestors. My parents and my family have therefore decided to have a feast when Bruce is next here and to tell stories about our departed nears and dears. This feels deeply satisfying and rooting to us adults. It is important to find ways to remind ourselves of the people who loved and nurtured us – to feel close to them and to keep their spirits and memories alive so that the next generation knows a relational identity, too.

With the insights of this chapter, I made a significant leap forward in the two weeks between acupuncture appointments. Abigail had readied a prescription of herbal supplements to boost my recovery, but I had suddenly improved so much that she no longer thought the herbs to be necessary. My biology was shifting with the inner work and the rest.

During my treatment, Abigail was startled to see a flock of Canada geese settle outside the window on the manicured lawn. They stayed for my entire session, despite the pinwheels set along the river bank to scare them off. I liked the presence of these graceful birds, so sure of their own navigation. Like living punctuation at the end of my ruminations on the bent tree, here was the arrow again – a community working together to move into and point toward the future.

Part of that future turned out to be finding a third trail-marker tree. A week into October, Hollis and I went looking for it, following our neighbor Polly's directions. He promptly found handholds in the bark and shinnied up to sit and then stand on the section of trunk that formed a natural bench, horizontal to the ground. I love that Hollis has this experience, connecting my childhood with his own. As a little girl, I could not know that my oak arrow would point in this direction toward my future son discovering his own *l'arbre croche*.

3 | Sleeping Bear

I N the great forests of Wisconsin, there once was a mother bear with fur gleaming black as night and eyes luminous with love for her two playful cubs. She was strong in body and spirit, both loving and beloved by all the forest dwellers, but especially by her own cubs. Mama bear nurtured them tenderly, teaching them to fish in the clear sparkling rivers and to give thanks for having enough to eat and a warm den in which to sleep when the sun went down.

One summer day, a great storm blew in and struck a tall tree with lightning, splitting the trunk with a deafening crack. It fell to the ground and ignited last year's dry leaves. The wind rushed through the forest and the fire whooped into life as more blazing trees fell with loud booms that terrified all the woodland creatures.

Crackling flames advanced toward the mother bear and her two cubs, driving them to the great lake for refuge. She was deeply afraid, but she courageously plunged into the cold waters of Lake Michigan. The brave little cubs followed their mother. The storm raged wildly, but they all swam strongly toward the horizon. The cubs trusted and loved their mother. She knew that safety lay this way where the raging fire could not follow.

The little family swam and swam, and the mother was comforted when she looked back and saw that her cubs were keeping up. Day turned to night, and eventually the protective gaze of the moon was again replaced by the gold of the rising sun. At last, mother bear glimpsed the forests of the east side of Lake Michigan. She found that her tired limbs had renewed strength when safety was in sight, but the two cubs were so much smaller and their little legs were very tired. They had no more strength. First one, then the other, sank below the waves.

Mama bear gave thanks when her paws touched the bottom of the lake. She pulled herself onto the shoreline pebbles and gave a mighty shake, showering water all over the sandy beach. She turned in joy to look for her cubs and worried when she could not see them. Mother bear sat down to wait. As time passed and they did not appear, the tears streamed from her eyes and she howled with the roar of a mother's grief.

"O, my children! O, my heart!"

The Great Creator saw the mother's grief and took pity. From the stirring waters of Lake Michigan rose two islands which the Ojibwe named the Manitous – north and south. Mother bear lay down on the shore where she could always watch her cubs in the clear waters laden with fish, as she had done when they had splashed in rivers on the western shore.

CരⴝⲬⰀ

When the original people paddled their canoes along the great sand dunes on the Lake Michigan shore, they saw mother bear lying there. They told the story of the great love and courage of the she-bear and her two cubs, passing the legend down from generation to generation. Today, it is published and told widely as local lore in northwestern lower Michigan.

As a child, I heard the story when we would visit the Dune Climb, the most popular access point to the dunes across from Glen Lake. Mom would pack sandwiches to eat at one of the picnic tables at the bottom and we would climb the steep 460-foot dune, admiring the views at the top, before galloping down at high speed. My parents hold my earliest experiences of the gigantic dunes in a photo of a gleeful little two-year-old me on top of the world as I created a huge sandpile at the summit above the enormous carpark, ranger's station, public restrooms, gift shop and surrounding forest and farms. Wind whipping my blond hair, I'm flinging sand with a plastic shovel as my beloved great aunt looks on with happiness in her eyes.

Mother bear must take comfort in the joy and wonder of children gamboling on her back. The reverence inspired by this gigantic dune, and the vista from its top over magnificent forests and pristine lakes, reflects the great heart of the she-bear. The pure glee of our racing down, bound after bound, feet sinking deep into the warm sand, is like her playful cubs. The awesome spirit of the wild seems embodied in these dunes and their legend.

The dunes are distinctive enough to endow their name on an expanse of lakeshore situated along the northwestern tip of Michigan's lower peninsula. The Sleeping Bear Dunes National Lakeshore extends along thirty-five miles of sandy beach and dune grass, and inland over 3000 acres of forests and historic farms. The glaciers are responsible for depositing great ridges of material as they receded, upon which sand has blown over the centuries.

As for the "Legend of the Sleeping Bear," it also contains a truth about the stunning shoreline that is deeper than metaphor. The story encapsulates the power and care of the Creator to bring peace to the bear. To Manitoba First Nation elder, Dave Courchene, the teachings of the bear center on the courage to follow the heart. In "Our 7 Teachings," Courchene explains that there is only one right path and it is found in the heart. The bear spiritually comes to offer the courage to do the right thing and thus to live the good life.

The Bear spirit assists the individual who then has a responsibility to the larger society. In the Anishinaabek social system, the bear clan members are seen as warriors and medicine gatherers, or as those responsible for defense and healing (Benton-Banai 76). The respect for the bear is so great that the Odawa and Ojibwe peoples understand her spirit of courage as one of the seven teachings that assist humanity.

CB&O

In a strange synchronicity, a black bear has begun to appear with frequency in our neighborhood this summer, a week after our arrival here in Michigan. From early July when we arrived through most of August, I was attempting to work and was suffering extreme ill health. We believe from our friend who lives nearer to the den, that this bear is female. Candace and her husband, Chris, have seen Tootsie since she was a cub, three years ago. Having identified her as female, they believe that there may be cubs next year.

Our cottage sits at a dirt crossroad, so close as to be almost on top of the intersection. Just across from our living room windows on Orchestra Drive, this black bear lumbered up and sat down in the road in early July. Our neighbors' bratwursts must have smelled pretty good.

Black bears have lived in this area since, probably, the late Paleoindian period, but they are rarely seen (Douglass 183). I have not been so knowingly close to a wild bear before, but this July visit began a series of sightings where she was repeatedly spotted making for our cottage. Just before reaching it, she no doubt left the dirt road to head down the bluff into the woods and toward the coniferous swamp where she makes her den. We frequently see a doe and two fawns take the same route.

Two days after the first sighting, our bear was seen again on Orchestra Drive at about 4:30 p.m. She was in motion heading toward our cottage, although she probably again veered off into the conservancy as she neared us. We began to think of a name for her. I proposed "Makwa" (bear), instinctively making the connection with Odawa and Ojibwe language and culture months before I began to read about the Anishinaabek. Our son, however, suggested the name that stuck: Tootsie Toes.

The Interlochen community at large then started to report how active the black bears had become this summer. One was frequently found in my parents' subdivision twelve and a half miles to the east. Another was glimpsed by a neighbor who was cross-country running about three miles north of us near the Little Betsie River. Closer to home, Tootsie Toes knocked down bird feeders by flattening their metal poles. As a result, neighbors brought in remaining bird houses, no doubt causing consternation to our feathery friends. Trash began to be set out only on the morning of waste pickups, but we still saw bearish evidence in the form of capsized plastic bins. No more barbeques or hot dogs over campfires. In the state park, campers complained of our bear. It goes without saying that we also continued to see her in our summer colony.

A month after the first sighting and after all precautions had been taken not to entice her, Tootsie was seen just before dinner a couple of cottages down from us. A week later, the bear sighting occurred at 8:30 p.m., about four hours later than usual. While a trio of neighbors were talking on Orchestra Drive, they looked up to see her when their leashed dog began to bark. Tootsie angled off the dirt road toward the conservancy, looked back, saw that Duchess – part German shepherd and part husky – was confined and resumed her ursine amble up the little hill toward our cottage. I was out around that time to take down the hammock, but did not see her in the dusk.

This last sighting was just before I took my medical leave. Since then, our makwa has not been seen in the colony, although she remains here as an unseen presence. I suspect that there are many times when Tootsie has visited, invisible to us, but seeing, hearing, smelling and knowing the whole community. Ten days after Duchess's bear alert, her owners saw our bear take on their bird feeder just outside the colony. (She won.) Candace and Chris had been putting the feeder out during the day and taking it in at night. To them, Tootsie appeared playful. She's wary of humans, luckily (it makes cohabitation possible), but she was also bold enough to take down their backyard birdfeeder in daylight and then to play with metal horseshoes, batting them from paw to paw. They know when she has made a short-cut of their lawn, too, because they discover a heavy glass pedestal on its side. She playfully whacks it as she passes.

Another sighting was three weeks later, on the day just after the week-long bear season closed on September 21st. Thankfully, she made it. A week later, she appeared again, aligning with the flip of the calendar page to October.

I wonder if the more obvious bear presence in 2020 is perhaps related to smell. *Science* writer Erik Stokstad links the increased animal sightings during daylight last spring to anthropause (humans being ordered to stay at home, causing forests usually humming with mountain bikes and trucks to fall silent). Yet in our area, people continue to enjoy the outdoors and bear sightings have also increased. Animals sense disease, stress and worry, as seen in therapy dogs and those canines who sniff out diabetes and cancer. More recently, the latter have been used to detect COVID-19 in the Helsinki Airport with complete accuracy and taking only ten seconds. French scientists discovered "'very high evidence' that the sweat odour of Covid-positive [*sic*] people was different to that of those who did not have the virus, and that dogs could detect that difference" (Henley; see also Grandjean).

While our family no longer had live virus in the summer, my liver enzymes had been malfunctioning, as lab work confirmed. When the liver stops working for a period of time, it cannot filter out sulfur substances that travel to the lungs and are then released upon exhale. Animals, with their more acute sense of smell, probably knew that my body was out of order.

Certainly, our cats know that we've been unwell. Till, our ginger Ragamuffin whom our son loves fiercely, suddenly began sleeping with Hollis when he was ill with COVID. Till would not leave the foot of Hollis's bed all night, raising his head to blink at the sudden light when we stole in to check on our boy. Arya, Till's silvery sister, has been doing the same for me.

Tootsie, too, seems to know and care. Why shouldn't wild animals seek to communicate with us? Bears have the most sensitive noses of all mammals, able to smell five miles away. Is it so farfetched to think that Tootsie, like the canines, can identify the smell of disease and that she would check up on us? In an interconnected world, this is not implausible. As I began to heal with the start of my medical leave, Tootsie stopped walking near our cottage, instead returning to her den via Candace and Chris's property to the south.

Traditionally, the Anishinaabek understand that Bear's spirit appears when we need her; specifically, when courage is needed to follow the heart. I imagine that the original people of this land might have responded to the honor of Makwa's repeated visits with the same questions that I had been asking about my health during acupuncture sessions and in my journals. More than one way leads toward healing. If I had understood Bear's appearance as do those who follow traditional Odawa ways, however, I would have reached comprehension more quickly.

For me, it required courage to take a medical leave. What looked like a logical decision to everyone else, backed up as it was by scientifically analyzed blood, was excruciating to me. It felt like a jump off a cliff into the unknown. It took Bear's courage – that majestic ursine energy – to step away from everything that I saw as giving my life meaning so that I could do what was necessary to heal. As I truly did not want to be ill for the rest of my life, I took the plunge and soon found that my leap was not a fall from the precipice, but rather like flying into a good life. Looking back on it, Tootsie made her appearance and persisted until I bravely accepted the medical leave and began to heal. Writing like this takes courage, too, for, as an academic, I am trained to analyze through the critical-rational intellect. There is vulnerability in heart words. Rather than offering assurances, this writerly path leads to the wild, too. I find myself recalling the arrow tree and its comforting bulk. Its material presence suggests that I am not alone; others have walked this path and, where there is one signpost, there will be others.

The autumn is a season of preparation for winter, of avian migration and chipmunks storing acorns. We pick apples and harvest squash during Bruce's visit. Red maple leaves dot the verdant moss and the sandy paths like cayenne flakes: crimson spice in a world about to enter its winter dormancy. Symbolically thinking about Bear's energy and lessons, it seems important that this is the time of year when she is at her strongest. Having survived the hunters and increasingly fattened by lake fish, berries, summer grasses and, yes, bird feed, Tootsie has until the first week of December to continue foraging before she makes a nest for herself by carving out the earth under a great swamp tree and entering her winter slumber.

The Ojibwe medicine wheel also connects the bear with autumn. This season is a time of introspection, associated with the evening, the west and the color black, which are all aspects of the turn to night. It is a time of transition into dreams and the knowledge found through our unconscious. To my way of thinking, this stage can be a pause for checking in with the heart so that life paths can be reevaluated and balance restored, not through the head, but rather through inspiration. Our bear has motivated me to lead with my intuition. We know of her presence, but she remains hidden like the spirit itself. When she hibernates in winter, she encourages us similarly to shift our focus and embrace our spiritual dream-life.

I wonder if we can see further relevance in that the constellation Ursa Major ("greater she-bear") points to the North Star, by which we navigate. The pole star, furthermore, also forms the tail of Ursa Minor ("lesser bear"). The Greek astronomer Ptolemy associated Ursa Major with the myth of Callisto when he catalogued the constellation in the second century. Zeus was not thinking of navigation when he tossed his erstwhile lover into the heavens along with their son, Arcas, to protect them from the jealousies of his wife, who was already so enraged as to have transformed them into bears. Nevertheless, generations of Western sailors, adventurers and hikers have steered by Polaris and associated it with Ursa Major and Minor, just as the bear spirit guides courageous inner expeditions.

I see here connections to minimalism – that movement to find greater value in life through decluttering. For me, it has been about paring back to make space for the lodestar to appear in this inner calm, like the expanse and quiet of the summer night sky over Lake Michigan. American poet, Mary Oliver, addresses similar feelings in "Driving through the Wind River Reservation: A Poem of Black Bear." "In the time of snow, in the time of sleep," it begins and then moves into the bear's perspective:

> Once
> she woke deep in the leaves under
> the fallen tree and peered
> through the loose bark and saw him:
> a tall white bone
> with thick shoulders, like a wrestler,
> roaring the saw-toothed music
> of wind and sleet, legs pumping
> up and down the hills.
> Well, she thought, he'll wear himself out
> running around like that.
> She slept again
> while he drove on through the trees,
> snapping off the cold pines, gasping, (3-16)

In many ways, Tootsie is herself my example. She does not join the mad rush of the "tall white" energy that wears himself out as he "[drives] on through the trees," not seeing the woke bear and destroying the pines in his hurry. I, too, have had that energy of overcommitment and pumping legs, and at what cost?

In contrast, this is "the time of sleep" (1). Oliver's poem captures the nature of restful calm. Unlike the arctic squirrel who hibernates deeply with a body temperature at below freezing, the bear maintains only a slightly lower body temperature than usual, lightly sleeping and waking. This metabolic shifting is necessary for her delayed incubation. Mother bears, like female sea lions, hold the fetus in stasis until it is ready to mature. This held gestation is not unlike the process that I feel deep inside of slow inner growth. Rather than being the frantic one who wears herself out "running around like that," I now observe those who do from within my own cozy den in the woods.

This shift of perspective interlocks with Bear's point of view, somewhat like the *taijitu* symbol of *yin* and *yang*. In what seems to be a companion piece to the above poem, Oliver's "Winter Sleep" wishes for a sisterhood with the she-bear that would allow them to hibernate together, cradled, "Like two souls / ... / Two old sisters familiar to each other" who "burrow into the yellow leaves / To shut out the sounds of the winter world" (4, 6, 8–9). Breathing together turns to "A shy music" (15) and from under the frozen snow,

> We would sleep and dream.
> ...
> Smiles on our faces, limbs around each other,
> We would turn and turn
> Until we heard our lips in unison sighing
>
> The family name. (20, 23–6)

The terminal line of the poem may refer to pregnancy, as mother bears gestate during hibernation. However, the "family name" is also the verbalization of shared dreams and limbs. "The family name" is what these entwined limbs and lips articulate through their unison and is itself a naming: the lips together form a meaning through their kiss. It is singular, emerging from a humanity in synergy with the interconnected natural world.

The family also emerges when it steps up to care and to cradle souls, which can and does exist beyond biological family. In Anishinaabemowin, ode (heart) is contained in ododem ("of my family"; clan) (Fontaine 224; McClurken 13). Thus "heart" is at the root of the extended family of the clan. Along with my doctor, my department chair encouraged me to take medical leave. It was a deeply compassionate act, for which I will be forever thankful. In my own natal family, my parents have stepped up to nurture me and their grandson, by helping him with his distance learning while giving me time to sleep. They are also passing down family ways, and our son has the opportunity to experience the great gift of a multi-generational family.

The family name is love.

ೞ⚭ೞ

We are now preparing to hibernate. The late warm spell during the third week of September was seventy degrees and sunny. I took the opportunity to refresh the inner partition walls in the cottage with a new color of paint: a nuanced grey that reflects the world outside. At different times of the day, the pigments seem variously to mirror the color of the tree trunks, the sky and the leaves. Gone are the long days of summer when sleep is shortened by circadian rhythm. Now, with October's arrival, the temperatures drop, and slumber assumes a new quality.

The cooling air sneaks through hairline cracks in the uninsulated pine planks that comprise the exterior and the interior of the cottage. We shut the sunporch door, let down the curtains to provide a little more insulation at night and wake fitfully at the unfamiliar sound of the furnace kicking on. But sleep is warm, cozy under duvets (down-filled comforters with a cover). It is a week when Bruce is in St. Louis and I have the bed to myself, mostly. One cat is under the covers, purring and soft-curled against my ribcage, while the other, atop the red plaid flannel bedding, presses into the crook of my knees.

Sleep lengthens in autumn. Waking now includes a long drowsy period of comfort floating between deep sleep and consciousness. In that state, there is some control over dreams. When fully awake, I often regret that I hadn't then conjured up wings, like the sea gulls at the lake who make air currents visible as they lift up, wings outstretched, gliding gracefully on updrafts.

It is dark, with only the moon lighting the squares of the windows. This is a new kind of chill, an enlightening cold. I think of earlier inhabitants of this land in bark longhouses and log cabins before the advent of central heating. They, too, awoke with a nip in their bones. I feel it as I rise to turn up the thermostat, the pine floor biting on bare feet. Then there's the gasp at the first hot sip of tea, the kettle having been caught just in time before its whistle wakes the house.

The shoulder seasons of autumn and spring are much longer in the north woods than on the plains. I'm still surprised in Missouri where a handful of sixty-degree days comprises all of autumn. In northern climes, the brilliant fall colors linger, the air crisps, woodsmoke tickles the air and the nose, and tiger-orange pumpkins flash in the fields against the yellowing land. At home, cinnamon-spiced apple cider and yellow sunflowers in tin jugs warm hands and hearts after picking honey crisps and playing in corn stalk mazes. Summer businesses stay open until mid-October for the final throng of tourists. These sight-seers drive Michigan's scenic Route 22 and the Tunnel of Trees overlooking Lake Michigan, where the trees mottle crimson, burgundy, mauve, fiery orange and pale yellow against coniferous green and the bright blue water. For a fortnight, the last blaze of color provides a visual swan song before the snow begins later this month.

After the autumn equinox, we linger longer in bed, making scurrying forays into the kitchen for steaming drinks and then drawing the curtains back to witness dawn. It is the weekend and we read in bed as we wait for light, then pancakes and maple syrup. Chores follow and afternoons at my parents' lemon-yellow house where the rah-rah-rah of Grandpa's football game on the TV mixes with the hearty aromas of Grandmama's baking, just as in my childhood.

It is the sacred time of rest in Judeo-Christian traditions and a day of fatigue for me. The latter is the main symptom in common for adult sufferers of COVID-19 along with headache. I was initially deeply frustrated by this extraordinary tiredness as it seemed to be hijacking my sabbatical plans last spring to conduct academic research and to rejuvenate through knowledge exchange. Luckily, I no longer feel like I was run over by a truck nor do I have debilitating headaches. Overdoing exercise does force me to stop for two or three days because of the resulting nausea. Mostly, however, I have learned my limits and am in a state of rest rather than fatigue.

My deep pull now is to hibernate, to dream, to exist differently. The courage of the bear – to follow my heart – is to embrace living just like this. How Western of me, thinking before that the product is the goal. Rather, the aim is a way of being.

It is a struggle to admit out loud that I want to stay in the woods, because I don't know what that means or implies. Is it a metaphoric pull? A colleague at a prominent research university observed once that tenure is granted when you know that the candidate can't stop publishing. That was me. Driven. The system shapes you thus. "Like many faculty members, I somehow became a silent workaholic. I do not believe that was a conscious choice," Associate Professor of Education-Policy Studies, Katerina Bodovski poignantly expresses in *The Chronicle of Higher Education* in 2018. Rather, as she explains in her article about her five-week collapse after a regular infection,

> many of us are socialized into this trait of academic culture. This is how things are done, goes the unwritten agreement. We prepare our doctoral students for that culture and advise junior faculty members on the job accordingly: This is how the institution works, and you'd better get ready for it.
>
> ... I used the word "silent" because being an academic is a pretty lonely job. Nobody else knows how much is on your plate.

I can identify. Usually, I awoke early, thinking about my research. If I began working at 4:30 a.m., I could get in a couple of hours before the household stirred. I identified my "self" through my work, which was all-consuming aside from meals with my family and the welcome respite of cheering for our son at soccer matches and baseball games. This attitude, oriented toward a "non-self," shortened my sleep and therefore my dreams.

Now what gets me out of bed?

Rather than arising in the depth of night to work, I embrace sleep. I want to be aware of shadowy trees silhouetted against the dark sky, the pinpoints of stars lighting the heavens and my dreams. And I want to find the bed crowded with partner and cats, and child as he appears, tousle-headed, book in hand, to crawl in. Giggling, he shows us a favorite passage, and we laugh and shower him with kisses.

ᏇᏝᏝ

Another bear sighting on October 1st, which Candace told me about five days later. She also revealed that our bear not only has an excellent nose, but that she herself smells. A long-ago tussle with a skunk lingers on her fur, like a warning bell on a cat. Candace said that when she's walking Duchess in the nearby woods, a slight stink of skunk prompts her to quicken her stride. It evens the playing field, for Tootsie can probably still smell our presence, having perhaps become accustomed to her own *l'odeur de la moufette*. We thus cohabitate without incident.

The Sleeping Bear legend is especially relevant because the mythic makwa lies down and observes. In September, when I was still able to walk only ten minutes twice daily, a friend asked if I might try pushing it up a minute at a time. I had to reply that my regaining health does not work like that. Pushing it makes me nauseous. This friend was simply reflecting what our medical system emphasizes as the norm for recovery from viral illness and that exercise is part of a healthy lifestyle.

In November 2020, *The Guardian* newspaper in London published an article by Linda Geddes about how long COVID shows many similarities to another post-viral condition, myalgic encephalomyelitis/chronic fatigue syndrome (ME/CFS). That month, the National Institute for Health and Care Excellence in the UK stopped recommending graded exercise therapy (GED), or "incremental increases in physical activity to gradually build up tolerance," for the treatment of ME/CFS because it can be dangerous to engage in aerobic activities when exhaustion continues or increases. The advice from the advocates at #MEAction refers to the similarities being observed between long-haul COVID and ME/CFS in the UK and further afield, including by Anthony Fauci, Director of the National Institute of Allergy and Infectious Diseases in the United States, during the press conference for the International AIDS Conference in July 2020.

Luckily, my own doctor has prescribed rest. My physical and mental health have been improving from contemplating the forested world and inhaling deeply the coniferous air filled with healthy bacteria. For me, health has not been about how vigorously I can exercise. When I've experienced fatigue or nausea after a stroll, I've stopped, rested, and not repeated the same amount of exertion again for awhile. As a result, I have experienced sudden improvements in my ability to exercise, as if I'm suddenly operating from a different, healthier plane. From walking a little on our city block every second or third day during the first three months of illness, I could suddenly walk ten minutes twice daily in July. In the autumn, I similarly jumped up to walks of twenty minutes, then thirty to forty-five minutes a couple times a week, seemingly from out of the blue.

On these longer ventures, I traverse roughly the same path as marked by the trail marker trees. Heading north to the state park, I pause to greet the special arrow tree of my childhood. I retrace my childhood footsteps, gravitating toward Wahbekaness where I stand on the bluff in the state park for long minutes, absorbing the view of forested shores, the movement of waves, the cast of light, and the waterfowl swimming or flying overhead. Leaves flutter and the gentle motion of Water Lingers accompanies the silence. I've had to learn that my health will build as I peacefully forest-bathe on the steep hillside overlooking the lake.

Like the sleeping bear.

4 | Mother Earth

WHEN I was a voice major at Oberlin Conservatory of Music in Ohio, my fabulous teacher, Carol Webber, would say that an opera singer burned as many calories as did a football player during a match. To the listener, good singing appears effortless and sounds angelic. For the singer, euphoria combines with a sensation of standing up to the sound. You learn to root to the ground because your physical frame is the musical instrument for a powerful voice. You must have excellent posture, firmly plant your feet, breathe with a ribcage that continues to expand during a sung phrase, and all the while keep your stomach elastic to flutter with individual notes. The zygomatic arch remains raised (the smile muscles) and the vocal chords execute passages with precision because of daily training. To sing on a professional level weds the ephemera of music at its most pure (a wordless vocalise) with the physicality of production.

As a double-degree student at Oberlin, both the conservatory and the liberal arts college counted me on their rosters. The "con" and the college were sisters under the Oberlin umbrella, but with separate admissions and degree requirements. Twenty-two students in our class graduated with both degrees; it took an extra year and a full load of maximum credit hours most semesters, but at the end we had a Bachelor of Arts and a Bachelor of Music.

The double degree was a smart approach if you aspired to professional music and wanted a fallback career. That was my father's stipulation if I wanted a conservatory degree. As a music librarian who had had a previous career as a professional horn player, first with the United States Army Band "Pershing's Own" stationed at Fort Myer during the Kennedy presidency and then with the Québec Symphony, Dad had experienced the reward of pursuing music while having a second career option. He is obviously an extremely good musician, but my parents wanted to raise their children in their home country, the United States. When they were expecting me, they decided that Dad would accept a position in the music library at Interlochen Center for the Arts. Dad always says that you can usually accomplish the thing that you most want in life. For him, that was giving his children an excellent upbringing by making Interlochen our home.

Music and the second career have therefore been part of my reality from *in utero*, but music was also the perfect counterpoint for my academic work. They balanced each other. Beyond the creative/intellectual synergy, singing well requires sleep, proper food and excellent hydration. Being fit and well-rested also laid the ground for success in academic coursework.

In hindsight, understanding the energetic flow in the body according to ancient Chinese philosophies makes sense of some of the healthiest periods of my life. The last align with when I was singing daily. In acupuncture, nurturing the spleen pertains to the earth, singing, the tissue of the muscles, the senses of the mouth, the stomach and memory. While I was vocalizing regularly as a student at Interlochen, Oberlin and Cambridge, my focus on singing, the mind and self-care meant that I also tended my spleen. While healing from COVID-19, my attention has turned to the *yi* of the spleen because it has been an area of deficiency. Considered to be the opposite of the *hun* of the liver where most of my health problems are concentrated, the spleen and the liver are connected and impact each other through that opposition.

Taxing my spleen may have begun in graduate school. I had first decided to pursue an academic career because I craved the scholarly work, and because it seemed to me that I could continue to sing. However, singing began to fall away as my schedule intensified with doctoral research and teaching. A trained singer needs to practice daily. I became frustrated when that couldn't happen because of the vocal fatigue of speaking for hours on some days, both in the classroom and in meetings. Already, I was bringing together music and Victorian literature as my research specialty – a sort of continuation of the double degree, but without the actual singing. It seemed the best that I could manage, and I made my peace with it. What I did not know was the extent that singing had helped me to maintain health on multiple levels. The spleen manifests pathologies as a result of thinking the same thing repeatedly (overthinking or excessive worry), according to Giovanni Maciocia. Not unrelated, overwork is another culprit. To find time to sing, meant finding a way to stay balanced in my life.

My busy schedule only increased to the point of becoming truly problematic later in my career. Working my way up the ladder from Assistant to Associate and then to full Professor, I began lunching over my keyboard without paying attention to my food or to taking a break. At home, too, I began to eat more hurriedly once I became a parent. "Please would you sit down and eat with your utensils." Forget relaxing meals – "Please would you let me finish my sentence" – with a small child present.

Ironically, the university profession as a whole does not reward the activities that nourish memory. Maciocia discusses how the spleen is cultivated not only by diet and exercise like qigong, but also through relaxed, regular and mindful meals. The *yi* of the spleen, he teaches, is replenished daily; we can assist this process through regularity in physical self-care. Doing so supports memory. A healthy spleen is vital for students and scholars. Yet time stamps of colleagues' e-mails reveal that the most research-productive academics tend to be either night owls or morning larks. I, too, stopped sleeping enough in recent years, regularly waking in the small hours of the morning with my mind already engaged. It helped my career to be ready to work before the household rose. Such a routine, however, habituates the body to awaking too early. It would have been much better to quiet the mind and return to sleep.

Now my spleen is not functioning well as a result of the attack of coronavirus on multiple organs. Closely related to the spleen is the stomach. By accident, I discovered during the summer that while over-doing exercise triggered nausea, eating an apple with peanut butter proved a corrective. Weeks later, my St. Louis acupuncturist informed me during a phone call that apples are tonics for the spleen.

On an embodied level, then, the world is relational. Singing promotes healthy thinking, liver and spleen rely upon one other, and wood interacts with air by absorbing carbon dioxide and releasing oxygen. Poetically, we see this interaction when the tree tops move in the breeze or when the wind shakes loose the leaves.

CB₩

All night in the deepest dark, I see nothing, but I hear acutely the sharp surprise of an acorn hitting the roof or the percussive patter of rain. With dawn, the windows reveal green with lines of grey – the trunks of trees and branches – and only a peep of sky. It is so intensely green as to seem water-like, but without the dappled movement of waves refracting light. The lower forest is motionless through the window. Just green. As undifferentiated as the vision of a new daughter or son.

The embrace of parental arms is not dissimilar to the natural world as experienced within an uninsulated summer cottage. I used to find it troubling to consider the earth as maternal. Its essentialism bothered me since identifying women with motherhood has led to the history of female repression and oppression. But in this natural embrace, I do feel intrinsic safety unlike anything but my mother's encircling arms. To me, the loving embrace of the earth makes me its daughter.

It is the first week of October and a plentiful acorn harvest crackles underfoot, making the stairs to the lake treacherous with their roly-poly abundance. Yellow pine needles layer in exotic fans on the boardwalk. The leaves – at the height of their spectacular color – whisper with the bracing air. As I step onto the dock, blinded by the dawn over the loons' cove and glorying in the sunlight on fluorescent red-orange maples, nature gifts me with an epiphany.

For six weeks now, I have been searching to internalize what the Anishinaabek understand as the spiritual presence within everything in the natural world. I understand how animals have spirits. Aesthetically, I enjoy plants, rocks and lakes in large part because my mother used to teach me close observation when we walked in the state park. She talked of the play of light, the roughness of bark, the smell of a broken mint leaf and the sonority of breaking waves.

As a child, I did not know that the enormous girth and height of the old-growth white pine, hemlock and red pine was unusual; it was simply the playground seen from my bedroom window. Only recently have I fully looked and thought comparatively, observing the height of the state park's behemoths in stark and abrupt contrast to the trees around it that form the second-growth forest. When I rode my bicycle from our house through the state park to elementary or high school, the staggering height of 120-foot pines was the norm. The rest of the world looked like it was populated with the small wooden trees that decorate toy railway sets. Words cannot describe what it means to know yourself small and protected by a forest of colossal trees; it shapes a world view that persists in after years.

With Mom, I learned how to touch, smell, look and listen in the moment for its own sake. Along with noticing individual sensations, I found that positive energy comes unbidden when you identify with natural beauty. Mom did not verbalize the latter. Rather, I absorbed a way of being because she taught me from toddlerhood to observe and delight in the environment. Perhaps something came *in utero* from her own positive feelings at walking in these woods and sitting by the same lakes during pregnancy. There are moments of mindfulness scattered throughout my days because of my mother's way of being and her teachings. This way of life naturally lifts the zygomatic arch in a smile as the heart sings with the surrounding world.

Last night, I was reminded of the work of three professors; their thoughts would prepare the way for mother earth's revelations to me the next day. Robin Wall Kimmerer's book, *Braiding Sweetgrass*, discusses the Anishinaabek concept of having two names: one public and the other true. Duck Lake and Wahbekaness seem thus to me, with Water Lingers being its true or "essential nature" (34). "Most indigenous place names," observes Anton Treuer have these sort of "deep meanings" of the geography that they describe (14).

Anishinaabemowin, Margaret Noodin further teaches, is a language mostly comprising verbs. These action words indicate systems of relationships just as the Great Lakes are a network of connected waterways.

Thus in one sense, my home is in relation with the larger world. The water of Wahbekaness travels onward to Wahbekanetta and the Betsie River, eventually reaching Lake Michigan and the Great Lakes as a whole, then on through the St. Lawrence river to the St. Lawrence Gulf. Here, it merges with freshwater from Canadian Shield lakes, and saltwater from the tropical Gulf Stream and the arctic Labrador Current, before entering the Atlantic. The link with Lake Michigan was a concept experienced physically by the original inhabitants of Interlochen when the band of Odawak wintering here travelled north on Lake Michigan to the two great summer villages of the Odawak at Waganakising.

Yet in a deeper sense, Wahbekaness indicates this place in particular. This lake is situated within a network of waterways, but its name indicates how the water is *being* within the landscape: it lingers. Wahbekaness is its individuated self (here, now, lingering). In future, some of its water will not linger. This moving water will become something else; its name changes as it flows into and becomes the Little Betsie River.

As I stand on the dock surrounded by Water Lingers, I think about how Kimmerer, a biologist and a citizen of the Bodéwadmi (Potawatomi) nation, discusses learning the language of her people. She had a moment of enlightenment as she puzzled through conceptual differences found in English nouns as compared to an Ojibwe dictionary. "A bay" in Ojibwe became the verb, "to be a bay." I will give her words about what happened next because they sparked my own understanding:

> And then I swear I heard the zap of synapses firing ... A bay is a noun only if water is *dead*. When *bay* is a noun, it is defined by humans, trapped between its shores and contained by the word. But the verb *wiikwegamaa* – to *be* a bay – releases the water from its bondage and lets it live. "To be a bay" holds the wonder that, for this moment, the living water has decided to shelter itself between these shores, conversing with cedar roots and a flock of baby mergansers. Because it could do otherwise—become a stream or an ocean or a waterfall, and there are verbs for that, too ... the language [is] a mirror for seeing the animacy of the world, the life that pulses through all things, through pines and nuthatches and mushrooms ...

So it is that in Potawatomi and most other Indigenous languages, we use the same words to address the living world as we use for our family. Because they are our family. (55; original emphasis)

When I stood encircled by the softly undulating Wahbekaness, I connected the dots with what I had read the night before. My own synapses zapped at being present with the water, as Kimmerer's did in simply thinking about a bay.

I was not expecting to have a revelatory moment on the dock, but I had undoubtedly hoped that at some point I would more fully comprehend how lakes and trees could be perceived as having a spirit. My wondering changed to wonder in a heartbeat as I stood in the morning sun, surrounded by water lingering. This is living water. The trees seemed to crowd in with individual presences, no longer blurring into a shoreline blazing with autumnal color. It was overwhelming, the aliveness of each entity, like 3D animation where perception deepens to make the three-dimensional subject reach out toward you.

Suddenly, my entire world view shifted. I was not the subject surveying the land. Rather, I understood how trees could "be tree." Water is living because it shimmers here for a moment, alive within these shores, springing up from deep in the earth and pausing before streaming into the Little Betsie River and through Mud Lake to Wahbekanetta ("Water Lingers Again"); along the main Betsie River and out into Lake Michigan; through the Lakes Huron, Erie and Ontario; along the St. Lawrence Seaway and into the Atlantic where it joins oceanic currents and tides. I was suddenly a very small being standing in a large animate forest and water system. It finally made intuitive sense how a person in pain or sickness could approach this living wild world and request aid. In the generosity of an ecosystem that gives of itself in order to support life, this animate world offers restoration to us – members of its family.

My approach – to seek healing in nature – shares quite a lot with the Anishinaabek belief that going into the wild and requesting aid will bring a response from those living forms that must be understood holistically as physical and spiritual. Repeatedly, writings by those steeped in Anishinaabek teachings reassure that the natural world does not care how you ask for help. There is no formula. The trees, animals, flora, mountains and bodies of water understand your heart and respond.

It is a blessing to be in a forest, to have the time and support to let go of the rushing world. I've been walking in this forest for fifty years and have only now, at the crossroad of physical/spiritual well-being, found that for which I've been looking. My mother's early teachings prepared me to look to the forest for joy. Living here quietly and observant, helped to position me. And then I went to the lake and I yearned to understand and to mend. Amazingly, both were offered.

Having basked awhile in the newly sensate world, I began the walk home with barely enough energy to climb the bluff-side stairs. The happiness coursing through my frame scientifically links to the human body's ability to repair itself. In a peer-reviewed article published in *Healthline* (2018), author Carrie Murphy cites Diana Samuel, an MD on the clinical psychiatry faculty at Columbia University Medical Center, to explain how the release of the neurotransmitters dopamine and serotonin into our brain and spinal cord causes us to feel joy. This chemical change in our central nervous system then positively affects our circulatory system, autonomic nervous system and smooth muscles (stomach, intestines, bladder). Samuel summarizes, "When something joyous happens, the emotional and physical response occurs right away because all of these things are happening simultaneously in the body" (cited in Murphy).

My sudden intuitive leap of comprehension regarding the animate world and its solace was unlike anything that I had previously experienced. It was a deepening of the contentment that Mom had first taught me to find in nature. Simultaneously, it was a new conception based on understanding animate nouns in Anishinaabemowin. It felt luminescent for its own sake, but there was also a scientific explanation. Joy "boosts [the] immune system," Murphy maintains, "fights stress and pain [and] supports longevity." It makes sense that I was so happy and then suddenly exhausted because the buoyant, transformative experience had essentially jump-started multiple systems and muscles. In my weakened state, I tired quickly precisely because my body was expending energy in healing. Three-dimensional trees seemed to crowd around, almost overwhelming in their solicitude.

With three hours of rest, I energetically righted. The same trees sway in their canopy like familial waving. They give me joy that feels like the generous love of a mother's embrace. No wonder people attuned to animate nature find their own sense of self and wellness through this synergy. It makes me never want to leave the woods. I only hope that I have enough time here truly to rewire before I sojourn again in civilization.

 প্রবৃ

When I wake now in the cottage, the world through the window is still a sea of green, but I newly perceive it as peopled by individual living trees, mushrooms, mosses, lichens, chipmunks, squirrels, pileated and red-bellied woodpeckers, jays, crows and black-capped chickadees – and these are only the visible beings just beyond the panes of glass. Kimmerer informs us that the Anishinaabek "count trees as people, 'the standing people'" (168). This perception rings true to my new way of seeing. The trees that I know are not just any trees, but rather *these* pines and hardwoods. We greet each morning together.

Imagine the identity crisis caused by the forced migration of indigenous people across North America to far-away reservations where the climate and topography were strange. To move cohabiters and custodians of the land meant trauma on a level that property-oriented settlers could not understand. For people who find joy in an animate nature, where each tree has a living individuality, it would be like losing family to be ripped away. There is shared history with particular trees, bodies of water, rocks and mountains. Memories are attached to this tree where my mother sat me or our lake where I swam, comprising both the event and its intrinsic feelings of joy and nurturing. This particular place and its natural inhabitants have stepped up for me, like a community of thoughtful people.

I am rewiring because of a language's ability to express different conceptions that have helped me to shift my perspective. Just think what happens when we lose languages like those spoken by the Odawa, Ojibwe and Bodéwadmi nations. Their languages are perilously close to extinction. If that occurs, then we simultaneously lose the conceptual key to the sort of awakening that I have just experienced and with it the extraordinary joy of becoming more aware.

Song celebrates such beauty. With music, the soul answers the earth's spirit. Unlike my formal vocal training of planting my feet and taking a breath to sing, the song of the earth now wells up within me in heartfelt thanksgiving. This is the music of unconditional love expressed through abundant life. The radiance with which my heart answers then offers something of my spirit, and this reciprocity reechoes in nature's responsive rejoicing. Kimmerer puts it well when she observes her undergraduate botany students as they hike back to their vans after spending several days in the wild: "There is a certain energy in the air, a hum. And then I hear it, someone singing, low and contented. I feel the smile spread across my face and breathe a sigh of relief. It happens every time" (235).

Western art trains people to smile in order to sing well. It knows that the best singing gives voice to the smile. But in the forest, song and smile occur together naturally, not because we are trained to use the smile muscles for good tone, but rather in reciprocal celebration. The Ojibwe put it thus:

In my song you hear my soul-spirit
In my dance, see its rhythm
In my ceremony, feel its depth (Johnston 134).

The third line here does not stand separate from the other two, like an item in a list, but rather unites them into a "depth" of multiple, interrelated components.

Anishinaabek rituals comprise healing songs and dances alongside plant-based medicines. According to Brenda J. Child, the Northrop Professor of American Studies at University of Minnesota and a citizen of the Red Lake Band of Chippewa Indians, "Ojibwe people organize their view of the world with plants and music coexisting in symbiotic partnership" (vii). In a synergistic world, song does not solely express the earth or, alternatively, the person's soul. "The Ojibwe approach to wellness link[s] the body to spiritual and emotional health," Child explains. In so doing, music was used to fix and make effective the herbs used for medicinal treatments and charms (vi, vii). To lose any one element of these interactive components invites illness. Joy and song naturally arise from existing in a beloved land where the medicinal properties of native plants are known, and where we feel wrapped in a protective maternal care.

N 12 September 1857, the worst passenger ship disaster in the USA occurred when the SS *Central America* went down 180 miles off the Carolina coast in a hurricane. Of the almost 600 people aboard the 300-foot sidewheel steamer, 149 survived (Kinder 200). 4700 pounds of gold from California sank, then worth just over two million dollars ("The Appalling Calamity"). The cargo included a secret shipment of "six hundred fifty-pound bar boxes, or ... thirty thousand pounds of gold," reports Gary Kinder, meant "to shore up the faltering northern industrial economy" (156). This staggering amount sent the United States economy into a tail spin, resulting in bank failures and depression both economic and emotional.

Some years ago, I happened to visit a friend from my student days at Cambridge who went on to become a rare coin specialist. Steve was working at Sotheby's New York office when the auction house was preparing to sell some of the recovered treasure. As we chatted in a back office, Steve surprised me by walking to the safe and offering to let me hold a gold ingot. It was fifty pounds, but felt much heavier. I could barely pick it up.

Some of the passengers of the doomed *Central America* had drowned because they lined their pockets with gold, Steve informed me, thus weighing themselves down. This anecdote horrified me as an example of the devastating effects of the "Mammon-Gospel," as Scottish philosopher Thomas Carlyle put it in 1843, "of Supply-and-demand, Competition, Laissez-faire, and Devil take the hind-most" (158). Gold not only lured men to the wilds of California, but it also seemed that they would die for it.

The story haunted me while I lay ill in Spring 2020 as an analogy for decisions being made by state and national governments to prioritize the economy over lives during the pandemic. As I read Kinder's gripping account of *The Ship of Gold*, however, I discovered a more sympathetic account of what happened: "some of the men had suffered great hardship since the summer of 1849 to accumulate the contents of that treasure belt or that carpetbag" (125). Several passengers did indeed pause to secure jewels and paper money before leaping from the sinking ship into lifeboats, and others hoped to take gold before realizing its weight, but most of the passengers valued their lives foremost. Still, Joseph Bassford attempted to fasten a money belt with

2000 dollars in gold before jumping from the deck of the *Central America*. Bassford had seen many of his predecessors falling into the water first before being hauled into a waiting lifeboat. His decision was therefore a risky move given the heft of the belt and the exhaustion of all the men who had just spent over twenty-four hours bailing water without respite. Even strong swimmers had difficulty when they fell into the water, weak from muscle fatigue and sleep deprivation. As it happened, Bassford failed to secure his money belt and it shook loose during his leap, sinking as he landed in the small wooden boat (Kinder 68).

The decision to leave the gold caused what Kinder calls a "hysteria": "one man ripped open a bag containing twenty thousand dollars in gold dust and sprayed it about the main cabin ... Others unhitched treasure belts, upended purses, and snapped open carpetbags, flinging the shiny coins and dust across the floor." A few threw newly minted double-eagle gold coins from the deck into the ocean (125). They valued their lives most, but to lose the treasure gleaned after years of sacrifice must have seemed almost farcical in the terrible situation in which they now found themselves.

There was an even more difficult road ahead. Many of the survivors eventually arrived home penniless and more than a few were in dire straits. Most of the thirty women who were rescued had lost their husbands in the catastrophe and were suddenly sole providers for young children in a period when employment opportunities for middle- and upper-class women were scarce. Some had no other family. Many more of the children were orphaned, reported survivor Jane Harris (Kinder 200). I suspect, too, that post-traumatic stress disorder was an ongoing issue for those who lived. Six decades before the traumas of World War I informed our present diagnosis of PTSD, there was a lack of medical support, especially for men suffering from what was then diagnosed as "hysteria," a catch-all term for a variety of female ailments. These hardships were, however, yet to come.

My point is that even while on a leaking ship in a terrible storm, it was not easy to choose between life and gold. It may be even more difficult in an ongoing pandemic. The novel coronavirus is causing a sticky, complicated and painful situation for considerations of both physical and economic well-being.

For me, the analogy of the ship of gold carries an additional sort of emotional wisdom. In the second week of October 2020, I read an article in *The Guardian* newspaper about the brain fog experienced by many COVID-19 survivors (David). This incapacitating condition can include migraines and memory loss. The precise nature of what is occurring is yet uncertain, but it has the attention of neurologists. What they do agree on is that various psychological and mental illnesses are caused by this coronavirus. It is debilitating to quality of life as well as the ability to work. In my own long COVID experience, I have had headaches that occurred when I attempted critical thought. With rest, this symptom has decreased, but I still need to remain careful not to overwork or the headaches and fatigue reoccur.

There is another psychological component to mending the body, which is less obvious than the PTSD linked to the trauma of being severely ill. I began to recover with the realization that unresolved emotional baggage is too much for my depleted state. It is like carrying around a thirty-pound suitcase when you are only able to walk – unburdened – for ten minutes. In my normal health, I do not notice the extra gold bullion, but right now it is pulling me under. For the respective survivors of the *Central America* and Pandemic '20–21, the load must lighten in order to become healthy.

The autumn epitomizes this process as leaves the hue of metal – gold, copper, bronze, rose-gold – spiral in the air to join penny-colored pine needles, revealing the contour of iron-grey tree limbs bared of these assets and outlined against a nickel sky. By this winnowing process, the tree lets go its plumage. I have always found a purity in the colors of a Michigan winter: the simplicity of grey or white lake reflecting the pale sky, black deciduous tree trunks and dark green pines capped with snow. It is a core beauty, pared back, not requiring gold leaf. Appreciating the autumn accents and then casting them off are part of survival and the life cycle; new growth cannot occur without loosening the brilliant trappings.

Still, it makes me sad to think of the bare branches that will emerge next week. I have so looked forward to the fall foliage and it has been particularly stunning this year. Normally, the colors come out one hue of the spectrum at a time: red, orange, yellow. This year, the colors mix together in a joyous burst against the deep blue lakes, creating a rainbow collage. Green conifers mingle with ribbons of fire that verge now and then on deep purple and burgundy. Old Mission Peninsula, famous for producing three quarters of the world's tart cherries, is at the peak of its harvest colors this weekend. Apple trees and vineyards are laden with fruit, wood smoke wends through the air, and quilt designs on barns complement the variegated leaves with geometric patterns. Colored corn cobs and pumpkins alternate with ghoulish porch displays and occasional mock-graveyards that sit in front of gingerbread-clad farm houses. Here is the bounty of the land, a patchwork tribute to the spirits of ancestors and a hunkering down to hot cocoa in front of the fireplace after the year's final, shivery picnics on Lake Michigan beaches. It is glorious and I have long missed this season here, where I grew up.

Autumn is both the time of fall colors and the loss of them; it is a season in its own right and a transition between summer warmth and winter cold. Michigan cottages stay open for the brilliant foliage and then are boarded up, the colony's communal well shut off and antifreeze poured down the drains. The tourist year closes with the glory of crimson sumac interspersed with browning ferns and grasses. The latter, the understory of the forest, always saddens me in its decay.

It reminds me of the state in which we must let go of emotional baggage. So does Gwendolen Harleth, the protagonist of George Eliot's final novel, *Daniel Deronda* (1876), understand necessary change: that which "she had been used to feel certain of in private life, was like a bit of her flesh—it was not to be peeled off readily, but must come with blood and pain" (II, 98). It can be excruciating to change something in which we have believed and invested, but that does not ultimately bring peace. Sometimes it requires catastrophe before we slough off the festering flesh. Then it turns a sallow browning and crinkling.

I so much want to be better that it is suddenly easy to see that if I am holding onto something that causes consternation and worry, then out it goes. In Chinese medicine, the lungs and the large intestine are associated with autumn, with bodily illness manifesting from grief and worry. The last two must be released, like waste that clogs the system. I think of the worries brought on by long COVID: what are the potential chronic problems that may reveal themselves with time? Just reading articles about long-term coronavirus opens the window to a rush of paralyzing worry and with it, another attack of headache and nausea. It is literally toxic to allow these fears into my system. Just last night, I found multiple articles linking high liver enzymes to the worst cases of COVID-19 in hospitals and the most dire outcomes. It may be that I had a very lucky escape, but it also worries me in terms of my prognosis.

In contrast, when I focus on healing anything that was preventing calm, letting go of the heavy gold of things that I had erroneously valued, this process lets in floods of joy. Automatically, I inhale. This serene reaction is a clue. Extreme worry, however, causes me to hold my breath or constrain it with a shallow breathing. This denial of air is another type of drowning, and we do it to ourselves without meaning to. I can only let go of certain baggage when I become so ill that survival requires throwing the ingots of false gods overboard.

CఞఴEౠ

Ever since my doctoral work, I have spent summers in England, Scotland and Wales engaged in the study of unpublished manuscripts and rare print books, in both public and private archives. This work forms the backbone of my published academic books and articles. London and Cambridge are my home bases, from which I journey to multiple destinations, including summer conferences. My closest friends have noticed that I'm usually in motion. We catch up over a coffee or a meal before I'm back to the reading rooms or dashing off to catch a train to Wales, Scotland, or the north or south of England. I'm always taking myself away, only to return to the people and places that anchor me. It is not unlike having an inner network of arrow trees that point the way to and fro, with some of the paths better travelled than others. Rather than holidays, these most frequented ways include both scholarship and friendship. You could say that I work and play hard, both. Yet, pocketed into this travel for work, there have been one or two adventures with friends that have been thorough holidays.

Perhaps the most memorable of these breaks occurred ten years ago when I sailed in the Inner Hebrides. Among these islands off of western Scotland, I became unencumbered in a manner similar to throwing unnecessary baggage overboard. At the time, I had taken a week off of summer research in the archives to go yachting for the first and only time with four friends: Jonathan and Ruth, her adult daughter Lucy and the latter's partner, Katy. My time on the sailboat, *Findeln*, is a useful contrast to the sinking ship and foreshadows my future, too.

From the first night when the orange globe of the sun sank beneath the mountains at Loch Drambuie, just north of Oban, across the Firth of Lorn and up the Sound of Mull, the landscape and ambient seascape spoke to me. It's an enchanting place of shifting, dramatic light, being so far north. When Jonathan gave me the helm and a quick lesson on navigation one day, it felt like guiding a living steed while the rider was also alive to wind and waves. I loved being on the water and quickly abandoned all pretext of reading while on holiday, preferring instead to simply be one with the sea, the light, the mountains and the easy camaraderie of good friends.

Our night sail was especially memorable, undertaken to beat a gale force 8 wind the next day on a section of the sea that was usually choppy even in the best of times, heading west of Rum and south to Tobermory. That Wednesday night, however, we had gorgeous calm seas at sunset as we emerged from the harbor of Canna, and unusual white clouds below the Cuillin mountain range on Skye. We spied caves while sailing past Rum, then the orange moon rising like an egg over Eigg before ascending past view into the clouds.

In summer, it never gets fully dark so far north (57 degrees north) and we stopped the boat one time (we were on the motor, 6.5 knots) when we saw a young basking shark appear before us. A porpoise arrived briefly, too, but the truly amazing event was when three dolphins began playing at our bow, diving below *Findeln* to leap up on the other side repeatedly, and then breaching on the port side, very close to the boat. The engine sound attracts them. They slow their pace in order to play alongside the yacht and perhaps satisfy their curiosity. How magical in the still night. Katy was so spellbound that she didn't notice when she bumped against the automatic helm so that the boat went all the way round in a circle. While Jonathan and Ruth were setting the course to rights, Katy and I were unashamedly more interested in spotting the dolphins, first on one side of boat, then on the other. At 1:30, I went to bed to the hum of the motor with a wooly hat pulled over my eyes because the chart light must remain on.

The next and final night, we sailed to Puilldhorain (Pool of the Otter), one of the most popular anchorages on the west of Scotland, just south of Oban. We'd seen more thirty-foot basking sharks and a porpoise. I'd relaxed during this holiday: roughing it with the wind against my cheeks, the spray of a rough sea, and achieving a oneness with life and therefore with self. Savoring every second, I stayed up very late talking with Jonathan that last night before sailing to Oban and then travelling the length of England to resume my research in Wells.

ᘓᘔ

What I could not know at the time of this journey of oneness with self, community and the sea was that it coincided with the birth of our son in China. He came into the world as I sat up late the last night, moored in the Pool of the Otter. Strangely, a significant part of that last night's conversation after midnight included the desire to be a parent. The true ship of gold was my precious little boy, Hollis.

Bruce and I traveled to China twenty-two months later to become a family through adoption, but it has always seemed miraculous to me to think that our son took air into his lungs for the first time as I breathed deeply the clear relaxation and peace of the northern mountains and sea. We both were splendidly alive as whole people before the next day when his own stresses began with separation from his birth mother and when I returned to civilization. It seems auspicious that he was born at a moment of my own serenity. Perhaps, equally, it was propitious that I could be at one with his purity of arrival into the world. Hollis's US birth certificate shows his birthplace as China and his parents as ourselves. It appears from this paper as if we had been in

China on that date. In a way, perhaps we were, as Hollis and I knew peace together despite our great geographical separation.

There's another, elemental connection between Hollis and me: we share dominant and subdominant energy types. According to the Five Element school of acupuncture, everyone has a primary and a secondary element. Ancient Chinese philosophies named the five elements: wood, fire, earth, metal and water. Knowing that my main element is earth and the second is metal plays a role in my treatment plan. Because everyone needs all five elements, a person is drawn to the other, non-dominant elements to achieve balance.

Symbolized by the white tiger, metal also relates directly to Hollis, who was born in the year of the white tiger. This rare Chinese zodiac sign occurs once every sixty years. The white tiger is one of the four spiritual creatures; it guards the west, a directional point also associated with the autumn and with the emotion of mourning. In horoscope terms, this metal tiger signifies power, wealth and leadership. I like to think that it is balanced by the gamboling dolphins during our night sail – animals of harmony and play.

Metal is more than it seems, for it becomes malleable and even molten when heated. In Victorian Britain, the term "Coals of Fire" (a reference to Romans 12) indicated the most sincere relationships within friendships and families. "Coals of Fire" was usually said upon being treated in loving ways after a perceived slight. Gentle corrections were understood as charitable acts that assisted each other to become better and therefore closer to spiritual perfection. When the daughter of four-time Prime Minister Gladstone declined the marriage proposal of Hallam Tennyson, son of poet laureate Alfred Tennyson, she wrote "Coals of Fire" in the margins of her diary and also the poet's pre-publication presentation copy of his important poem, *The Lover's Tale*. With this gift, it was as if he vowed that the family would continue to treat her in the most generous terms, despite their heartbreak. She recognized this, as shown when she twice wrote "Coals of Fire." To offer fraternal correction in such situations was perceived as like the fire that metal workers used to correct impurities. Such treatment usually made friendships firmer in nineteenth-century Britain, as it did for the Gladstones and Tennysons (Weliver, "Coals of Fire).

When I realized that multiple acupuncturists identified my secondary energy as metal, I had to chuckle, for I have investigated "Coals of Fire" as part of my academic research and writing. Before this understanding of my nature had been offered by a holistic health practitioner, I had gravitated to unpacking these "metal" qualities in nineteenth-century Britain. Offering gifts of loving correction can be seen as an economy; they nurture the human spirit through a system of personal exchange that was perceived as a counterforce to the rise of capitalism, rapid modernization and the attendant human abuses, including poor working conditions and back-breaking hours. Economic and industrial advances were applauded even as leading statesmen, society hostesses, clergy, academics and artists expressed concern regarding the attendant ravages to the human spirit.

Today, our family is blessed to spend more time together than usual in our woodland cottage. Normally, we leave for our jobs and winter home in St. Louis in early August. Warm summer air means open windows and lake swimming up to the time of departure. This year, however, Hollis and I are staying until the shared well is turned off in the colony and then moving in with my parents. I plan at that point to return to the cottage during the days to rest and recover within nature.

In preparation for the cold, I have just finished installing removable insulation. The upper walls and ceilings of the cabin remain their bare rustic wood, but along the bottom of the walls I have fixed a wide band of reflective aluminum – a bubble wrap covered on both sides in shiny, pixelated foil. Aluminum is a useful tool of basic survival in cold temperatures, not a token of commercial exchange. Similarly, the most valuable commodity as the *South America* went down were life preservers made of cork and tin. While our society has made metal into the basis of economic exchange and therefore monetary wealth, at its elemental level metal is a substance of energetic conductivity. Aluminum may be one of the commonest metals, but for me it is far more valuable than gold because it amplifies warmth in the northern woods. It also bestows a modern-rustic feel, which I rather like.

This aluminum was the closest thing that I could find to the foil that I used in my flat in Hove, England, when I was a doctoral student at University of Sussex. My housemate and I lived at the top of five flights of stairs, just above a historic crescent of Georgian houses that peered out over Brighton's boardwalk, colorful beach houses, pebbly seaside and derelict West Pier, first opened in 1866. Our two-bedroom apartment was even more drafty than most English accommodation because our top story was directly exposed to winds off the English Channel. Unless we stood at the windows to watch the water or were visited by the occasional errant seagull flying high, it was the cold salty air that reminded us that we dwelled seaside. In the winter, we lined the inside of our windows with cling film (Saran Wrap) and blow-dried it to melt the edges of the individual sheets together. We affixed aluminum foil sheets behind the radiators so that the walls reflected heat instead of absorbing it. It was still so chilly that I wore fingerless wool gloves while writing up my doctoral research.

By way of comparison, our Michigan cottage requires neither cling film nor gloves. The thermostat is low to conserve heat, but it is not uncomfortable as in my student days. When our cottage wall furnace expels heat from the bottom, it hits the aluminum insulation and bounces back into the room. It then rises until it is pushed down by the ceiling fans, rotating clockwise. We've closed off the window-lined sunporch to conserve heat, but its gorgeous light and views remain accessible from the living room through the windows that form the top half of a double-wide Dutch door to the sunporch.

Having begun this chapter with the anecdote of the lost gold ship, then moving through the auspicious sailing in the Hebrides and the cold of Brighton beach (Hove, actually), it seems fitting to end with the grounding that I am finding in our home, now cased with an aluminum hull in this sea of green. I like to think of our aluminum as not only insulation, but also as one of the five elements. Here's the wood of the cottage and the outside trees, the fire of the furnace, the metal (aluminum) and water, or the sense of being in a ship sailing in the mossy green of the earth toward Wahbekaness. In the calm of our cabin in the forest, we can transform grief and disease into something else, like the metalsmith's burning cleanse, shaping pliable metal into fresh forms of beauty.

was surprised this morning at the lake to find that the dock and raft have been taken in for the cold months that lie ahead. It would happen at some point, I knew that, but it still startles me to find myself landlocked, or interlocked (between two lakes). Now, instead of relaxing in the Adirondack chair on the dock, lake surrounding, I perch on the raft beached three feet from the gentle waves gradually eroding the sandy shore, surveying multi-colored hills on the other side of the lake. The fulsome ovals of orange, gold and crimson mix with a few purple smudges where a tree stands bare branched. Falling leaves whirl past, creating a miniature flotilla on the surface of the water. When I take our cats out, harnessed for a walk, our silky mink bounds and leaps at the leaves while her camouflaged brother – caramel like the fallen pine needles – crouches, waiting to lunge at passing chipmunks. As Ragamuffins (an American breed), our cats are very trusting and it is unsafe to let them out without supervision. They would not know to protect themselves against predators.

With the seasonal transition, animal behavior changes. Two nights ago, we awoke to the eerie howling of coyotes in the distance. Bruce is visiting and we were both unnerved by the sound. Just before dawn today, a pack of these animals ran down Orchestra Drive yipping loudly to the accompaniment of the whines of an animal in distress, startling us awake. We're thankful to be in our beds in the cottage and not out hammock or tent camping. Tonight at about 7:30 while Hollis was still up, we listened to the sharp yipping again. Coyotes move in small groups. Their howls can sound three to five miles away and serve as locator beacons, but these yips are a much closer, family experience. Probably, the parents are teaching their pups to hunt. These creatures are more active in autumn than in spring and summer when the young keep everyone near the den. With the cold, the pack begins to move together in search of scarcer food, mostly small mammals. Household pets can be targets when outside and children are also occasionally at risk. Accordingly, Hollis and I agree that if he is outside by himself, then he'll cycle rather than play on foot. Eating outside is forbidden; even an apple or a sandwich can lead the coyotes to associate human beings with food. It goes without saying that we also determine to keep the cats close to us when they are outside, rather than securing their leads to a nearby tree while we do outside chores, like hanging laundry to dry.

Hearing the coyotes makes me feel closer to seasonal changes than I had previously. When I visit my parents' winterized house, it feels at a remove from the natural world. The windows there frame a lovely lawn, blue spruce and maple trees, cattails, a pond and a ring of houses regularly spaced around the picturesque water, rich in fish, frogs and turtles. A lush ecosystem flourishes in their suburb, but with its manicured landscape and curated trees it is removed from the wild. Insulated walls and central heating, moreover, keep life temperate.

In our cottage, however, we are nestled in the woods and close to the lengthening nights and the chill, as if within a tent of wood. The temperature now drops to thirty-nine degrees Fahrenheit at night with a daytime high in the fifties or sixties. We pile on duvets and conserve energy by lowering the thermostat to sleep, waking in the morning to turn on the heater and return to bed until it is warm enough to shower and breakfast. Without the stress that truncates my slumber during working life, I sleep deeply and fully, awakening to hear the fluttering leaves like an offer of conversation.

The morning chill reminds me of childhood visits to my maternal grandparents on their northwestern Pennsylvania farm. In the winter, Grandpa would rise first in the Victorian house, which remained unheated at night and shook in high winds. Lying awake, I could hear him downstairs shoveling coal into the furnace to start the trickle of warmth up through the registers. He headed out for the first round of chores before breakfast as the household gradually stirred. We took turns in the only full bathroom before assembling for a breakfast of eggs and homemade sausage from the farm pigs.

There were no coyotes howling in the distance, but there was a closeness with animal life that comes from listening to the calls of livestock and feeling their humid warmth as they are fed and milked in a drafty barn. As the barn cats and kittens received their share of steaming raw milk, so do my cats get fed first in the cold morning before our family gathers at the kitchen table. Because cats are not pack animals, this order does not really matter to household peace; behavioral issues do not ensue as they would if they believed themselves to be the head of a family pack.

Coyotes, however, are hierarchical creatures. As a dog-owner, Abigail told me that packs of wild canines, wolves and coyotes wait for the alpha male to eat a little first before he gives way – stomach not yet full – to the others in the group. It reminds me of the gracious behavior of my own extended community. I discovered yesterday that one of my esteemed older colleagues gave way to me. He was aware that my taking medical leave had caused me the pain of giving up my graduate seminar. In our department, we only have the opportunity to teach a graduate class every two years at most. Besides offering coursework-based instruction, these seminars help students to select their doctoral dissertation directors. My generous colleague knew that he would not be taking on new doctoral students so close to his retirement. He mentioned his decision as being made for the good of the department (the pack, if you will) and for me. He offered to exchange our courses, giving me the graduate seminar and taking for himself the entry level undergraduate class that I had originally been assigned. Such a magnanimous gift opens my heart to my colleagues.

The experience of the family pack, too, seems to include parents stepping up for their children. As Bruce and I witness our ten-year-old's virtual learning experience and explore other options such as homeschooling, I begin to suspect that we will need to soft-pedal our own ambitions for the good of our pup's emotional well-being and education. Instead of focusing on over-extending ourselves in domestic environments that are ill suited to the many activities that suddenly occur at home during a pandemic, I am thinking of time with my son as precious for connecting in a way that we would not otherwise have had.

There is a reason why the American Academy of Pediatricians recommends one hour of screen time up to teenage years. By the end of five to six hours of daily learning through the computer screen, Hollis has turned into Robot Boy. He's unable fully to participate in human interaction. In England, primary schools that are entirely online for now are only giving three hours daily screen time, plus a lot of independent work. A colleague who specializes in child psychology told us that childhood learning occurs best when there is a relationship, which does not occur through virtual education. Given that in-person education risks infection, and that CV-19 has proven disastrous to our family, she responded enthusiastically to the idea of homeschooling: it would limit the screen time and promote relational learning.

My friends have also been supportive of the decision that we made to homeschool. "Congratulations on doing what you feel is right, taking control and seeing beyond the educational equivalent of processed food," one messages me. They understand our decision as "strong and principled." We realize that it will be a lot of work, but so is facilitating virtual learning.

As a parent, I am motivated by protective feelings. When I was writing in the chapter called "Mother Earth" about being a daughter, my dominant feeling was of love and safety, of being embraced and helped. In my own maternal emotions, love has always included wanting to keep Hollis safe. This is not always easy because our son is a runner. He was racing around when we first met him and has not stopped (aside from illness). Soon after we became a family in China, we gave him a fuzzy green frog backpack, which was actually a disguised child harness with a lead attached. He loved Froggy and as a result we did not lose him at twenty-two months in the Beijing airport nor, at age three, did he rush onto the London Underground tracks.

Now it is duck hunting season and on weekends we hear the violent p-p-p-p pop-pop pop-pop-pop-pop of rifles. I dislike this hunting of the surrounding wildlife, but the reality is that forest management goes on around us. So Hollis and I wear florescent orange now when we walk or cycle to keep us safe from our own kind. (I can now cycle about a mile and walk ten minutes twice daily.) Donning neon, reflective clothing is what it means to be savvy in the bright autumn woods.

଼ଞ୍ଚ

Almost psychedelic in its multicolor vestments, the foliage annually attracts hoards of weekend tourists from downstate or Chicago. These sight-seers often do not step away from the wineries, the public scenic views or each other to learn the precautions of wild Michigan. We do.

On a family walk in the conservancy last week, we three found the bleached mandible of an animal. It was a long white jaw with teeth intact. For me, Ted Hughes's "Relic" immediately came to mind. This poem begins, "I found this jawbone at the sea's edge" (1). While our found jaw was left by its hunter instead of being washed up by the sea, the second stanza fits our experience more perfectly:

> And the jaws,
> Before they are satisfied or their stretched purpose
> Slacken, go down jaws; go gnawn bare. Jaws
> Eat and are finished and the jawbone comes to the beach:
>
> (6-9)

The circle of life centers on the jaws of prey and hunter together ("the jaws / ... go down jaws;"). In the first stanza, the speaker introduces this idea with the cold deeps of the ocean: "In that darkness camaraderie does not hold" (5). If this mammal that we three are peering at – at its jaw, that is – went down because of a coyote, it would have done so in the dark of the early night or before the first glimmer of dawn. Camaraderie between species does not hold for creatures at the base of the bluff atop of which our cottage sits. Its warm lights gleam upon approach, but remain unseen in the forest depths. A rich biodiversity – the *wild* life – is part of our land conservancy.

Today, as I crossed the boardwalk over the swamp by myself, intent upon the lake, I paused at a small bird's wing lying across the slats. Grey feathers intact and connected to two bones from the body, it is picked clean, feather shafts gleaming white and only the faintest remnant of maroon gore attached to the bones. Could this be evidence of the coyotes' wild rumpus last night? And could the fish head that we three found at the dock a month ago signify a longer residency by the pack? Coyotes maintain a carnivorous diet of fish, fowl and four-legged mammals, unlike the pescatarian bears who concentrate on flora, fins and fruit. Here is evidence of the circle where one life gives to another, and a reminder to respect the romp of the wild. We need to be aware of nature's manner, not to tame it but rather to coexist.

The lake, too, offers this lesson. In an earlier chapter, I mentioned how parents here prioritize water safety for their children. We play in the lakes, but with respect. As winter approaches, we caution our young about hypothermia. There was a tragedy in my teenage years when an older boy took a canoe out on the spring lake, just thawed from months of winter ice. He ventured out without telling anyone and capsized. Hypothermia sets in quickly in these northern waters and he drowned in Green Lake. The event still horrifies those of us who remember.

Today, the wing reminds me of that young life just taking flight. My path blocked, stomach twisting, I turn around. This is not the day for the lake.

∞

The coyote is a strangely appropriate animal to make its appearance now. The pack arrived unbidden, surprising us and causing us to reevaluate our lifestyle choices in order to respect their presence. Their appearance also startles me into grappling with what I can learn from this animal. In acupuncture, coyotes as canines might be associated with the pericardium. However, I am thinking about them as pack animals; they are not watchdogs, a topic that surfaces in Chapter 11.

I have never really thought much about coyotes before, yet Coyote is another potent symbolic character in indigenous American legends and stories. Barry H. Lopez calls on American Indian folklore in his cross-tribal collection of Coyote stories, *Giving Birth to Thunder, Sleeping with his Daughter: Coyote Builds North America*, to support his statement that this prankster hero is a composite of particular "powers," "habits" and "acts" more than a physical Coyote. Sometimes tribes give these attributes to the Great Hare (Eastern), the Raven (Pacific Northwest), the "First Creator" and Original Man (Lopez xv).

To Carl Jung, the trickster is "a bestial and divine being, whose chief and most alarming characteristic is his unconscious" (143).

Teachings about Coyote involve learning through laughter. Tricksters caution children not to behave like Wile E. Coyote in the *Looney Tunes* or, through frivolous verbal play, frothy songs and lewd gestures, they impart elusive or dangerous truths. "This fellow is wise enough to play the fool," observes Viola after meeting Feste, the jester in Shakespeare's *Twelfth Night*, whose talent lies in being a "corrupter of words" (III.i.60, 35). However, as Lopez shrewdly observes, not all folk stories need to moralize; sometimes we are simply entertained by the dark, greedy, lustful and ridiculous aspects of human nature. Humor lightens our burdens (xvii).

In Anishinaabek traditions, this mischievous figure is named Nanabozho (Manabazho) and is part of creation stories. In the story of maple syrup, for example, this half-deity corrected the laziness of the people who no longer tended their crops, firewood, traditions or each other. They favored, instead, "*lying beneath maple trees with their mouths wide open*," in Robin Wall Kimmerer's words, "*catching the thick, sweet syrup of the generous trees*" (63; original emphasis). As a result, Nanabozho watered down the sap so that considerable labor would be required to obtain the sugar.

Nature is playful, too, like Coyote. On windy autumn days, gusts sweep down low, kicking up the fallen leaves in a swirling upswing – a gravity-defying dance that counterbalances the wild circular sway of the canopy. Coyote is elemental like this – primal and childlike. I think of our boy-on-the-go, our son whose energy and hunger seem equally boundless. Of course, the earliest developmental emotion is hunger. Being fed translates as affection and effective communication: food answers the cry of hunger. Similarly, the coyote parents have hunted for their young and are now teaching the pups to feed themselves.

All animals nurture their offspring thus, but young children are also like the spirit of Coyote. I am thinking of our son's incessant bathroom humor, his delight in waiting around corners to startle us and his creative, if shocking, attempt to put together the swear words that he has variously picked up.

Still, Coyote makes me pause to consider what I am missing in trying to shift Hollis away from poop jokes or scaring his grandmother, which she really does not mind (much). Original Man is found in the primal elements that we try to smooth away to help children to learn how to behave in civilized society. I vow to delight more in the prankster side of our son in order to accept Hollis at his level and then, after he feels heard, help him to scale up to more civilized behavior.

Coyote reminds me of elemental laughter and the delight in the prank that is found in human nature. Hollis asked me last night why April Fools' Day could not come more often. Indeed, why not? I suppose it does in different guises. We focus on Halloween treats in twenty-first century America, but this holiday is traditionally also the time for tricking. As winter approaches, we acknowledge the transitions and releases of the natural world with ghostly rituals (Halloween, *Dia de los Muertos*, Ghost Suppers) and with celebrating the autumn colors as the trees begin to let go their leaves. With the cold weather come indoor gatherings and family-made entertainments. If we turn off our technology, we look to each other for occupation. Out come the stories, music, baking, crafting and games. Children's jokes elicit appreciative laughter, while their attempts to startle us shake things up on their terms. It's empowering for little ones.

More than a stepping aside for the good of my child, the unexpected lesson of homeschooling is the way in which it helps me to grow in my life, too. The prankster reminds us to lighten up. In these days of increasing professional loads coupled with Zoom meeting fatigue and managing our children's schooling from home, we need very much to step back. The time to create a prank – to lie in wait – requires us to slow and to use another part of our brain. How similar to our cats when they crouch, pause and wiggle in preparation for the playful pounce. The prank is all about connecting or relating to those who are physically present. Contact with others is precisely what is in short supply during social isolation and quarantine.

03&0

We had our Ancestors' Dinner last weekend. Outside, the leaves flew off the trees to land on our heads, to swirl in the air and to blanket the ground. Branches bared themselves, opening new vistas through their limbs.

A family in large part hangs together through its culture, memories and traditions. For me, this foundation provides the present with some stability. It's unusual in our busy lives to stop long enough to request the memories and life lessons of the older generation. Doing so offers respect and value to our elders along with reaffirming our own sense of pack identity.

Over a pot roast with trimmings, my mother talked about her closeness with her mother. Her father and three brothers did the outside farm work while Mom and Grandma Phyllis baked and cleaned. This mother love was passed on to me through learning to make bread, cakes, pies and jelly rolls. I had not fully realized until our Ancestors' Dinner that baking carries this inter-generational meaning for my mother. Rather than a gendered division of labor, to her it meant close mother-daughter moments. Suddenly, I saw greater meaning in the time that my mother spent with Hollis, teaching him to make a cherry pie and to roll cookie dough. Tears come to my eyes. I want that with him, too; making time together to pass on the family recipes. Perhaps this cross-generational activity is especially important for Hollis's sense of belonging, given that our family is created through adoption. You are what you eat.

We certainly connected again with our departed relatives through the stories. Out came remembrances of the gruff jokes that Grandpa would tell at large family dinners.

"The last time I used this pocket knife," he would invariably say in a loud voice that carried to the kids' table, "was to clean the manure spreader."

"Ew, gross," we'd squeal as he sliced off a large wedge of cheese.

At other times, he would impart to us children, confidentially, "Lettuce, turnip and pea." We giggled and puzzled over what it actually meant to turn up and pee.

We also saw afresh during our Ancestors' Dinner. My mother told how her maternal grandfather taught her to tell stories by transforming real people into characters. While I was growing up, Mom would similarly tell stories to my brother and me about Ricky Rabbit who would hide on our yellow school bus, curious about where we went and what we did. Our lives, told from Ricky's perspective, never failed to delight. This glee had us kids peeking over our shoulders the next day to catch a glimpse of our rabbit companion. He was careful not to be noticed (we never did see him), much like the wildlife around me today. In a way, the family story-telling continues as I look at reality from the point of view of nature as animate and interactive.

We observed in the days following the feast that Hollis began participating more readily in the pre-writing for his schoolwork. Through listening to the family stories, the act of story-telling became his own. He discovered that he, too, passed on family identity when he told a story because we have a focus on particular approaches, from gruff jokes to long stories peopled by us and our animal companions.

Remembering ancestors at a feast naturally brought up the topic of other shared meals. I learned that in Harlingen, Texas (formerly "Six-Shooter Junction"), the Sunday dinners of my father's youth comprised Mexican food. It was a regional heritage, adapted by my non-Hispanic grandparents when they lived near the southern US border. Originally from Indiana, they moved to Texas while Dad was a small child. Once there, they would set a day aside for the complicated preparation of enchiladas. I was accustomed to thinking of our family ties extending in the opposite direction, to French-speaking Canada where my parents lived in the two years before I was born and where my uncle's family permanently settled. Besides having cousins whose first language is French, I grew up with little bits of Québécois in our family patter along with material culture like a wooden toboggan and Christmas tree ornaments of Bonhomme, the representative of the Québec Winter Carnival (a snowman with a red tuque and French-Canadian arrow sash). It is somehow completing to learn of Mexico, too, a heritage that my paternal cousins have more acutely through forebears on their other side.

Put another way, time creates a sort of Möbius strip, where ancestors' stories are our deepest memories from our youngest years. These stories root our hearts, our identities and what the Chinese know as *ching*. Acupuncturist Giovanni Maciocia describes the last as the precious essence inherited from our parents and stored in the kidneys. The *zhi* of the kidneys gives structure and balance to our minds and emotions. It is considered pre-natal, ancestral *qi*, but it also has a forward movement. Kimmerer expresses something similar when she discusses the Anishinaabek sense of time as tidal, not linear like the river (206–7). Thus a single legend of Coyote served as both the Anishinaabek creator myth and, circling round, a prophecy: something to guide the future.

Spirit stories are living because they contain all time, Kimmerer explains. They were original teachings, are conduct guides for future behavior, and are pleasurable in the moment. I am still grappling with this idea, but Coyote's appearance three times just when I needed to learn the lessons associated with the trickster encourages me to pause and consider.

C恩O

I do not really want to relinquish my sleeping bear mode of unconscious hibernation. This internal state recovers and nurtures my own soul. With Coyote, however, I realize that the movement has begun. My acupuncture session this week revealed a change, too. I am now balancing both the delicate newfound intuitional state (the inner *yin* to the Chinese) with beginning to reach out to *yang*.

Acupuncture perceives an interaction between the flow of *qi* in the main channels (which can be likened to a network of mountain streams) and the extraordinary vessels, thought of as:

a wetland reservoir lying in the lowlands. In the spring when the streams are full, the wetlands absorb the overflow of water. In times of drought ... the wetlands act as a source for filling the streambeds with needed water. Throughout the year, the water in the streams and all of its living organisms constantly interact with the wetland. (Wang 280)

This aptly-named "extraordinary" system can be a focus for treating mysterious symptoms and chronic disease because it provides extra resources when the main channels are depleted and receives run-off in times of pollution or blockage (Wang 283). Of these extraordinary vessels, the *wei* and the *qiao* each have a *yin* and a *yang* component.

My pulse, Abigail told me, had previously placed me firmly within *yin wei mai* (the *yin wei* vessel). Now with Coyote, I am transitioning to *yang wei mai*. This progression can be understood holistically as beginning with the innermost aspect of self. The Chinese pictogram for *wei* "means to connect, tie-up, integrate, or maintain" and "to safeguard" (Wang 292). Put another way, the *yin wei mai*, by being linked to an acupuncture point for the pericardium (the layers of membrane surrounding the heart) nourishes "the deepest inner environment of the body" (Wang 293). Going a step further, *yin wei mai* might be understood to be oriented to the inner self since the *shen* of the heart is also the *shen* of the whole person.

If *yin wei mai* is the "inner gate" (*nei guan*) and thereby associated with *what* we think ourselves to be, then *yang wei mai* has to do with the "outer gate" (*wai guan*); it integrates the reservoirs with the "triple burner," a conceptual pathway of *qi* and fluids running through the body (Wang 293). Abigail suggested that, in psychological terms, we might think of the *yang wei* vessel as comprising *how* we think about ourselves; *how* we think about what we are.

As I have learned from Coyote, I do need to remember to find inside myself the place where fifth-grade humor seems funny, where I can offer connection and love, and where I can focus on teaching my son culinary arts, as the coyote pack instructs its pups on hunting. As I move forward in the next chapters, this balance between the inward *what* and *how* of self, the nourishing *yin* and stimulating *yang*, continues largely through contemplating animal encounters. The spirit of the coyote, similarly, is often understood as a mirror to reflect on life direction and to consider if it needs a tweak.

Put another way, existing primarily in aspects of self that are most inward looking (*wei mai*) is like the change that occurs when the dock is winterized. I still visit the lake (metaphorically the *shen*) daily, but my perspective has shifted from the dock surrounded by water to the beached raft, firmly on the shore. My seat and my view change as they did with the ancestors' stories, but I still commune with the same water.

Like Coyote, healing from long COVID requires us to remember to embrace being human, including our limitations. During Pandemic '20-21, most of us cannot accomplish at our accustomed pace, even if we remain physically healthy. At very least, we have additional cooking, cleaning, children's education, and the stress of neither enough alone time nor relaxation in the physical presence of friends. Heeding Coyote's lessons means remembering to laugh even while living through a gritty reality.

For me, the illness has pared me back to bare branches and I feel rather small, exposed and humble. Such moments can lead to prayer. A friend who is a medical doctor recently mentioned to me in his quiet way that he might begin to pray for the first time.

"I have found prayer to be helpful," I offered just as quietly.

The thing about prayer is that it acknowledges a person's relationship with something bigger that defies our comprehensive knowledge. It acknowledges our personal limitations even as we find the courage to invite aid. Coyote, as a creature who represents both divinity and primal humanity, also encapsulates where the two meet.

Prayer positions us to request and then to look for help to arrive. It orients us toward a symbolic reading of the world around us. When things happen that have never happened before (like becoming aware of the ongoing presence of a black bear or three consecutive visits of the coyote pack), we can dismiss them as coincidence or we can choose to reflect upon them. On the simplest level, the last is beneficial because we consider what we have yet to learn. For me, this acknowledgement of a helpful animate world inspires deep gratitude for this earth which supports us in myriad ways.

I can now cycle about two and a half miles and, on the same day, walk twice for ten minutes. The next day, a mile-long walk only tires me rather than initiating days of nausea, as occurred a month ago in September. When I feel tired the day after that, I stop and rest. Slow progress, but I am thankful. In particular, it is good to be able to make it as far as the arrow tree now in my walks, which I make a goal. I reach it, contemplate it for some time, and then retrace my steps.

☙❧

It was heartbreaking to unenroll Hollis in school. The parental responsibility for these educational choices humbles me. Since prekindergarten, this particular school has given our son a truly caring education. We have all loved it.

Today was an emotional day with the sadness of saying good-bye to this dear school at morning meeting. I held my cub while he told friends how to contact him and then I led the first full day of homeschooling for him. What a successful day of learning! I'm sure that there will be difficult moments along the way, but the benefits were immediately apparent. Our ten-year-old was his fun-loving self again, eager to learn, fairly independent and with a manageable schedule. He was even able to relate with us at the end of the day. How different from the long hours of daily technology during virtual learning that left him slack-jawed and glassy-eyed. Already, homeschooling seemed to be a silver lining of the pandemic. Interesting: I had never had that thought about virtual learning.

Sleeping Bear was a guiding force in the decision to homeschool. As Mama Bear, I responded protectively to my cub, drowning in a virtual world and losing contact with others. Now we nurture as we educate him through strong family relationships. Unfortunately, I am not strong enough to do all the home educating. Grandmother Bear will facilitate his learning going forward this autumn. My involvement has helped his transition at the beginning, but it left me with thick fatigue by day's end. I retired to the cottage and within a short time, the forest proved restorative yet again.

I had expected the following days to be transitional. In actual fact, homeschooling was immediately so much better that there was no transition. We had a boy once again who could interact with us all day long. He's buoyant and such good fun.

When we had talked in preparation with Hollis about what he would miss about school, he said, "The technology."

We thought that this could not be true for he has articulated in the past how much he cares for his friends and that he would like to continue all the way to college, if only the school didn't stop at fifth grade. When I probed a little more, it turned out that Hollis disassociated the two experiences of school. There was pre-pandemic school where he had emotional relationships and then there was virtual learning, where he had technology.

Yesterday, I took Hollis out for a drive since most revelatory conversations occur while he is in the back seat.

"So, what is it about the technology for school that you like?" I began.

"The efficiency."

"Hmm," I replied noncommittedly. (Sounds like something that he's heard; technology definitely had not been efficient.)

Pause.

"And the ads."

(That's more like it.)

In an even tone so as to elicit as much information as possible: "What ads?"

"On the links. They're mostly for insurance and toddler clothes."

"I don't understand. What links do you mean?"

"For math – like the measuring volume assignment."

"Isn't that odd," I replied, staying calm. "Normally, ads are geared toward the audience. I wonder why insurance and baby clothes ads are popping up."

"There was one for bras," came the voice of innocence from behind me. "It was really weird. These women were jumping around looking happy. The bra was two colors." Pause. "I clicked on the button to say that I didn't want to see it. Then I left a comment in the comment box."

"Oh? What did you say?"

"This is inappropriate."

Indeed.

ha-ha is a visual illusion found in eighteenth-century British landscape architecture. With such a feature in place, the vista from a country house seems an uninterrupted expanse of verdant pastureland dotted with sheep or cattle. In actuality, a steep bank keeps grazing livestock away from the great hall. The ha-ha cultivates the appearance of pastoral harmony so that civilization looks like a world without fences.

One of the most visited ha-has is at the back of King's College, Cambridge, although in this case a river replaces the ditch. Standing at the west end of the famous fifteenth-century chapel, the Cam river is hidden by a steep bank. Three or four bovine placidly graze in a field, seemingly keeping their distance by gentleman's agreement until a punter's pole swinging up and down in the water disabuses the notion. Viewed from the other side of the field with the cattle in the foreground, the perpendicular gothic spires of King's College Chapel arise incongruously out of an apparently wild pasture, especially now that a wild flower meadow stretches between the chapel and the Cam.

The splendor of Cambridge's architecture often appears curious to me. Here is King's ambitious Tudor stonework and the Fitzwilliam Museum's imposing neoclassical front rising out of the flatness of the fens. It reminds me of the opening lines of *The Mystery of Edwin Drood*, Charles Dickens's incomplete final novel: "AN ancient English Cathedral town? How can the ancient English Cathedral town be here?" As the narrator queries "the real prospect," we realize the opium haze through which he peers. In fact, he imagines his rusty bedpost as a cathedral spire (39). Cambridge is not a cathedral city, but rather a spired market town of the fens. It amazes me to think of its grand buildings firmly planted on bits of solid land amid the marshes.

Similarly, the ha-ha is both a matter of deception and perception. In its illusion of reality, this garden feature is rather like the experience of long COVID. As with most long haulers, I was a physically fit person before contracting the novel coronavirus. While I had paused my usual aerobic exercise to heal from an ankle injury in October 2019, as of January 2020 I was cross training again with five to six miles of daily cycling and walking during my sabbatical in Cambridge. Countless media narratives of long COVID begin with examples of fit young people suddenly so fatigued that they have difficulty rising from bed. Such accounts of well-toned athletes establish that the chronic condition is real even when tests do not reveal results that can account for the symptoms.

Like the ha-ha, perception occurs when you realize the deception. In terms of the disease, deception includes what we were told about COVID to begin with (its official symptoms comprised fever, cough and shortness of breath) and the misleading idea that testing is fully accurate. While we all, understandably, wanted to find a stretch of solid ground, the fact is that so little was known about this novel coronavirus that many aspects of it were missed, underreported or misrepresented.

My patient experience was often one of having to advocate repeatedly for testing and treatment of our son's symptoms which were not yet being recognized, but were potentially very serious. In spring 2020, my primary doctor and some ER staff at one of the St. Louis research hospitals took us seriously, while Hollis's physicians at another facility played down his (and my) symptoms. I was stunned to realize how this situation persisted the following February when Hollis's new pediatrician opined that COVID-19 was little worse than a cold; argued that long COVID did not exist, especially in children; and scoffed when I mentioned the UK House of Commons debate on long COVID, including for children. He was, however, puzzled at the combination of symptoms in the obviously unwell child sitting before him, scratched his head, and could offer no other diagnosis.

It is as if those inhabitants of the stately home deny the existence of the ditch and that anyone is in it. We had to make multiple visits in the spring before the initial pediatrician and her colleagues would agree to run tests. Time and again, I had to advocate for our son while myself feeling extremely ill, calmly saying to various doctors over and over again:

> I am a trained academic, I am rational and not hysterical, and I recently returned from a Level 2 country. These are our symptoms. I have been in communication with medical doctors in both the UK and the USA, and they are seeing cases like ours in England and in Chicago ERs. It is appropriate to run these tests. Please do the tests so that we can rule out other potential diseases and have a baseline recorded to measure against in future.

The whole system was a mess. Hospital personnel told us that their protocols were changing daily. When we telephoned, we were often put on hold while nurses read through the guidelines as issued that morning.

It was only weeks after we became ill that the Mayo Clinic began to recognize dizziness as a symptom of CV-19, followed by the inflammatory disease for children, MIS-C. We eventually got the necessary care for our son at the ER of an excellent research hospital. By the end of the summer, all of our symptoms were recognized as aligning with COVID-19.

Still, long COVID sufferers continued to be disbelieved by many doctors who discounted the reality of patient experience, causing a delay in testing, increased anxiety and a worsening of already debilitating fatigue. As of December 2020, *The Lancet* medical journal called for better acknowledgement of the "scale of the problem" of long COVID. To begin with, "health professionals must listen to patients to understand their concerns, validate their experiences, and manage their symptoms and comorbidities, referring patients as needed."

ः

I contracted CV-19 when I flew home from a sabbatical in England, where I had been for the first months of 2020 at the University of Cambridge. My return to the USA in mid-March came earlier than planned because of the rising infection level. England was declared a Level 2 country just before I left. The morning of my flight, I awoke to the heart-stopping news that President Trump intended to close the border with continental Europe the next day, except for US citizens returning home. Four days later, he made a similar statement about the UK border. As it transpired, international borders did not entirely close although requirements such as negative test results and quarantine upon arrival have severely impacted the airline industry. Of course, we did not know this at the time.

Sabbaticals come around once every seven years in American universities. They are competitive awards for professional development and renewal, which usually means working on a significant research project or engaging in knowledge exchange. I was pursuing both as a Visiting Research Fellow at the Faculty of Music, University of Cambridge and a Visiting Scholar at St. Catharine's College, Cambridge. The latter was also my undergraduate Cambridge college, where I feel truly seen now, but which had originally seemed as illusory as the ha-ha and as insubstantial as the fens.

I write this twenty-seven years from the week when I arrived as an undergraduate at Cambridge and almost immediately committed the first of many *faux pas* during Michaelmas Term. At the porter's lodge, I enquired where I might purchase a "robe" for formal hall (dinner). With raised eyebrows, but impeccable politeness, the porter informed "Miss Weliver" that a robe was a bathrobe and that I was perhaps interested in a "gown."

Thus began a surreal experience that felt like being on a film set, including the matriculation process whereby new members officially register for their degree and subscribe to the statutes and ordinances of the university. First came the matriculation photograph. The first year students assembled in alphabetical order, seated on risers and neatly dressed in black and white under the college BA gown.

The click of the photographer's camera was accompanied by a throng of tourists poking their Nikons through the black grills of the front gate. St. Catharine's main gate is the only open courtyard in Cambridge, no doubt contributing to our reputation as the friendly college. When you know that this open side was meant to be finished and, furthermore, that it was originally the back of the college, the openness seems more like exposure. I always found it a disorienting break of the fourth wall to be photographed walking to the library or simply sitting with friends on the benches in main court. Our life was occupied in reading, thinking, writing, debating and living in this ancient seat of learning, while we were simultaneously examined curiously, photographed and later pasted into scrapbooks and photo albums.

From having the official matriculation photograph taken, we trooped into the dining hall where the senior tutor sternly admonished in his matriculation address that drug use would not be tolerated. Then, sympathetically:

"I'm sure that you think that you don't belong here."

Yes, I was sure of it. As an Affiliated Student, I was meant to complete a second BA at an accelerated two years. It was a full-time coursework degree that concentrated on one field of study (English literature in my case) and was therefore closest to the US master's degree. I had just taken two years out to work and save money for my next degree, however, and I was nervous about whether I had become rusty since my Oberlin graduation. It seemed unreal that I would now find myself a Cambridge student.

The senior tutor, Dr. Carl Baron, seemed to be speaking directly to me with his sympathetic statement, so much so that I do not remember what came next. Paul Hartle, who was then my director of study and later became Senior Tutor, tells me that Dr. Baron's comments were pretty much par for the course for matriculation addresses. Paul's own "emphasised Socratic humility and Donne concerning the huge hill on which truth stands, together with a small jest about '*matricula*' – an unidentified small fish, according to the OED" (*Oxford English Dictionary*). While the Praelector would follow with a more serious explanation that "matriculation" originated in the Latin *matricula* (a list), Paul felt that an unidentified fish "would no doubt encapsulate" how the undergraduates were feeling – and how the dons were also feeling about the students – until we all came to know each other better. He ended by focusing on "the obligation to look out for and after each other."

From here, we freshers would sign the matriculation book. I like to think that it was kept since the college was founded in 1473, but I don't really know. What I do remember was that I paid more attention to my signature than usual and it still came out looking unimpressive. When, I wondered, would the other shoe fall in my Cambridge existence and the college realize the great gaff that they had made, for surely I did not belong here.

Later at the first of our grand college feasts, Matriculation Dinner, I made my way through the bewildering array of cutlery by following my neighbor's example. Heavy silver candelabra and salt shakers adorned the middle of the table; embossed nametags and plates with college crests lined the long edges, and dark oil paintings of founders and past masters hung overhead. The dons' table was raised on a dais running the width of the room while the students' three long tables were on the main floor, extending the length of the hall. Conversation proceeded with deliberation, and questions and responses developed slowly, fully shaped in the mind before carefully considered responses fell from the lips.

It turns out that I was not alone in the impression that my admission to Cambridge must be a mistake. Many of the people who became lifelong friends later admitted to profound loneliness at the beginning of their time at university. No one dared to say aloud this feeling, a silence that only deepened the isolation. Was this the proverbial British stiff upper lip? Just get on with it. Soldier through.

However, it may be that my experience was more extreme, for I was foreign. Frequently, I was unable to hear what was said to me (unfamiliar accentual patterns delivered softly), a situation that invariably had me urging friends to sit with me in the front row of university lectures where I had a better chance of hearing. This also meant arriving early and watching as porters in black suits and bowler hats washed the blackboards with sponges and buckets of water.

In the following weeks, my behavior or comments were – it appears – embarrassing. I was the only American in our college. My schooling in English norms largely came from a shuttering of the eyes by the person to whom I spoke, by which I knew myself to be in breach of decorum. My acquaintance would be too polite to tell me what had happened and I was too shy to ask. Only in exchanges of sheer surprise was enlightenment offered, as when I finished one anecdote with, "I almost had a cow!"

"You almost had a wot?"

It was then explained that while Americans may have cows, the English have kittens.

Ironically, what finally made me realize the reality of my experience – that I had not suddenly been transported to a film set – was a Merchant-Ivory production. In the first term at Cambridge, I used to escape to the Arts Cinema, then located off Market Square in the town center, just a ten-minute walk from College. For two hours, immersed in American speech rhythms, life was normal in pace, accent and culture. It always surprised me to emerge from the cinema, blinking, into a Cambridge of precisely spoken Queen's English.

In late November, I went to a showing of *The Remains of the Day*, which focuses on the servants in a great English country house. As Anthony Hopkins lays the long dining table, precisely measuring with a ruler the placement of plates, cutlery and crystal in relation to each other and the table edge, it suddenly clicked for me. If Hollywood made a movie about the silver service of the upper one hundred, and it looked just like a Cambridge formal hall, then I must not be in a film. The movie industry was portraying my reality. With that realization, Cambridge became solid. My point of view had shifted.

To those outside elite England, Cambridge cannot but seem unreal, a deception like the appearance of pasture running unbroken from the manor house. Aurora Leigh in Elizabeth Barrett Browning's 1850 poem of the same name experienced something similar when she moved from her mother's mountainous Italy of sublime "grand nature" to her father's England:

> On English ground
> You understand the letter—ere the fall
> How Adam lived in a garden. All the fields
> Are tied up fast with hedges, nosegay-like;
> The hills are crumpled plains, the plains parterres,
> The trees, round, woolly, ready to be clipped,
> And if you seek for any wilderness
> You find, at best, a park. A nature tamed
> And grown domestic like a barn-door fowl,
> Which does not awe you with its claws and beak
> ...
>
> I could not be unthankful, I who was
> ... holpen. (1:627–36, 646–7)

I was likewise thankful to be "holpen" by this university founded in 1209 with the motto *Hinc lucem et pocula sacra* (from here, light and sacred draughts / precious enlightenment). Cambridge is a cultivated world that nurtures inquisitive minds, advances knowledge and beautifies the earth, literally and figuratively. During my late afternoon study breaks, I strolled in hidden gems of horticulture, following paths behind closed gates, discovering jewel-bright patches of hidden Eden, somewhat like Aurora Leigh's surprised outsider sense of "nosegay-like" fields "tied up fast with hedges." This "nature tamed" was then simply so unfamiliar as to appear a deception.

When I eventually left England six years later, however, doctoral work completed at University of Sussex and myself marinated in formative British experiences, my feeling of wholeness depended upon the UK. It turns out that as I got to know the college better, Paul's sentiment of helping each other superbly encapsulated St. Catharine's character. Just before our final examinations, for example, Paul thoughtfully placed an encouraging card in each of his students' pigeonholes and for graduation bestowed a volume that he'd found during his rambling in second-hand bookshops. (Mine was Carson McCullers' *The Heart is a Lonely Hunter.*) As I later learned during my sabbatical, lunches in college were opportunities for the dons to exchange information with each other if they felt concerned about a student. Is it any surprise, with this level of attention and care, that I feel understood at Cambridge?

I went on to live mostly in North America, but to return to England for full summers and sabbaticals. My professional partnerships, the archives and, yes, the dinners and intellectual fellowship, bring me back annually. It was truly heartbreaking to have to cut my sabbatical short in Cambridge because of the pandemic for I had been resting and rejuvenating in a deep-seated way, along with researching and exchanging information with colleagues. I had never before left "England's green and pleasant land" (Blake 16) without knowing when I could return. This last was what was most devasting because it impacted my sense of self, including the many nurturing ties of friendship that made up my relational identity.

The significance of my return to my roots in Michigan in order to heal, therefore, really begins with the fact that I had been floating between two worlds: I am American born and raised, but with cross-Atlantic interests, education, friendships and personal history. To be forced to find my footing only in America meant rebuilding that side of my identity in order to regain health. Rather than homogenously blurring the distinctions within self, I had to reclaim my childhood.

Educational systems reward adaptation and, to an extent, I had never stopped being an ex-pat. While at Cambridge, I formed close friendships with other women from overseas, most notably from the Bahamas, Sri Lanka and Japan. We were all outsiders. Because I could pass as white British until I opened my mouth, I did not have the additional experience of skin-color racism. However, it's still off-putting to overhear snide comments about Americans in pubs and cafes, or to have first-time acquaintances try out terrible American accents on me. At Cambridge, the latter were so poorly executed that I was only aware of what was happening when the speaker invariably ended his or her statement with "God damn," as this expletive was apparently an indicator of American speech.

We four overseas friends puzzled together about the Cambridge examination system. The class of our degrees and therefore our future prospects entirely depended on how we did in the final-year examinations. In the mock exams at the end of the first year, our marks were not as high as we had hoped. We were therefore worried. There was something that the English educational system had taught, which I and my non-English friends did not know. A nameless something. We didn't know what it was or how to ask for it. We worked to learn the unknown something by paying anxious attention to the written comments on weekly essays. Somehow we did it – all of us received good marks – but at an additional struggle, unseen by the dominant culture. My area of study, moreover, was English literature, which required deep cultural awareness as part of the textual analysis.

I don't think that it even occurred to me to balance somehow between two identifications, keeping separate the American and the Cambridge. Having completed my doctorate in England, moreover, the procedures of graduate education at the US university where I am now employed are learned instead of second nature. Sometimes when I still feel that I don't fully belong, my accent confuses things because it sounds like I am at home.

With this context in mind, imagine what it was like to leave England with the belief that borders were closing, as if in preparation for war. After traversing an eerily quiet Heathrow on the morning of my flight, I sat in a sparsely-populated aircraft and snapped a photo of the receding coast of Wales. Who knew when I would be able to return to friends, colleagues, archives and favorite haunts? Since the age of twenty, I'd been living a transatlantic identity, first during a semester abroad as an undergraduate at Oberlin College and Conservatory, followed by six years of English education, and then twenty years of professional trips to work in archives. For the first time, I was about to be forcibly grounded: unable to travel easily because of the pandemic and, unfortunately, about to become too sick to leave my bed.

cs8o

Now, with a sudden "ah ha," the world turns topsy turvy again. Unexpectedly, I am finding my footing in the USA as well as the UK. Thus the metallic plane balances with the forest's nurturing, for I locate my lost self as a result of aircraft and arrow tree both pointing my way home.

What I thought was a retreat to the north woods to convalesce is now looking like a permanent shift away from a cluttered, stressed-out mode of life. Thoreau got it right when he called himself a "sojourner in civilized life" (199). I, too, hope to carry the transformative health of the woods with me when I return to work, for returning to my childhood home has helped to ground me in a positive way: I have planted my feet in the soil and, like the arrow tree, stretched in unexpected directions before reaching again for the sky. John Bailey, in discussing how his Odawa band understands the significance of bent trees, confirms that the trees were seen as special and even spiritual, whether their form was the result of disease or deliberate manipulation. His people "would see (the tree) and offer a prayer" and then utilize it (cited in Puit). Thus humanity and nature come together, physically and spiritually. It was precisely through being diseased, grounded and still looking toward the heavens that a sorely needed recovery of self has occurred, resulting in holistic health.

Knowing how likely it was that I would come in contact with the virus either in the air, London Heathrow or Chicago O'Hare, I had arranged with my family to quarantine for fourteen days from the time when they picked me up. My husband, Bruce, stopped for groceries and library books on the way to St. Louis's Lambert Airport, barely leaving room for my baggage in the car along with us three passengers.

During the next thirteen days, we attempted to adjust to our working life at home along with assisting our son in distance learning. We took it in shifts and yet it remained challenging given the small footprint of our two-bedroom house. Groceries arrived from Amazon Prime. Well, half our order arrived along with strange substitutions, such as neon yellow macaroni and cheese in place of frozen corn. We periodically drove to nature reserves for a welcome escape. Our hikes were so socially distanced that we rarely saw another human being. When we did, the lone figure was far away on another tree-lined ridge.

On day thirteen of our quarantine, Hollis and I skipped stones together on a sparkling creek outside St. Louis where pink magnolia trees bloomed. These little spots of normalcy, joy, and letting off steam in the sunshine did us good. Then we walked a gorgeous trail along the limestone ridges. As we made our way along the steep forested ascent, we were astonished to see wild turkeys take flight.

"Did you know wild turkeys fly?" we asked each other.

Hollis complained of tiredness, but otherwise we felt much better for our hike. With one day of quarantine remaining, I was relieved that we were almost free from concern.

On the morrow, however, we all collapsed with debilitating fatigue and headache, along with various other ailments. The symptoms differed for each of us. While Bruce mostly recovered over a long weekend, Hollis and I spent most of the next three months bedridden.

On the Fourth of July, we were finally well enough to drive to our summer cottage in Michigan. The stunning firework displays as we travelled into the night on Independence Day aligned with my emotions at returning to my childhood home. Hollis still tired more easily than normal, but he now began a steady improvement. Nauseous, dizzy, tingly, headachy, fatigued – my symptoms lessened in early July, but I was still quite ill no matter how much I tried to convince myself otherwise.

In the Michigan summer, I tried to return to daily life. I wasn't ready. Normally, I run to relax, the steady stride changing the rhythm of my internal clock like a meditation in movement. My overactive mind exchanges stress for endorphins and dopamine. It reminds me of Maciocia's discussion of the illness that results from the over-stimulation of alcohol, tobacco, films and video-games. What the Chinese call jollity is what we might term pleasure-seeking in the West. Stressful jobs, by almost requiring high levels of aerobic exertion or other modes of escapist relaxation to manage the level of stress, layer together various types of overstimulation. Fast-moving modern life seemed to require quick fixes. The ability to both overwork and over train depend upon a person's balance and reserves. Because of COVID-19 and its ongoing symptoms, I had drained these energetic reserves. With nothing left, I had to learn to sit meditatively in nature until my body achieved a oneness with my surroundings.

Now, however, I observe the rustling leaves and the rippling lake, attentive to varied motion in sight and sound. With time, it is actually fairly easy to come to a feeling of center in a place of natural beauty. The difficulty lies in allowing oneself to do so without self-blame or imagining external criticism. It is a shrugging off of the values of our capitalist, ambitious, career-driven society and daring to figure out what it means to be one with (our) nature.

Much of my process has been to learn to trust what I see in this natural world; this faith is difficult for an academic who does not speak easily about the love that we can see in wildlife and the generosity of the trees. But this is the treasure – the gold – of this earth. As John Jennings puts it so aptly in his words to H. Owen Reed's tender choral piece, "Michigan Morn":

> There is gold in the eye of the morning, in Michigan where I was
>   born;
> There is gold in the sky and the lakes and the trees,
> For a man with a will to believe what he sees; (1–3)

The sunrise casts a golden glow, but "gold" also expresses what is valuable. The "will to believe" is not deception, but rather insight to the riches of the land and to perception itself. The song concludes: "There is gold in the eye and the sound and the touch, / And the heart of a Michigan morn" (17–18).

It reminds me of how simple truths are often the most insightful. Similarly, uncluttered expression often reveals the most impressive thought. Here, sensory perception itself is golden, but so is what it perceives: at heart, Michigan mornings are precious. There is no deception or trick of the eye like the ha-ha. Instead, we find our place through contemplating and celebrating that nature, too, has a heart.

AST night, I laid down every rug that I could find over the freezing floor from bedroom to bathroom: green bathmats, red braided throw rug, and even the maize-yellow striped rug rolled for storage. It was forty-five degrees inside when I awoke to a cat curled under the red flannel bedding, snugged into the curve of my back, and the other cat sitting above me with the expressive, unblinking stare that clearly required, not requested, breakfast.

So comfy in bed – warm – but I walked the rug-bridge to the bathroom where the cold of the tap water shocked me awake. It was thirty-three outside and the pipes reflected this temperature. I briefly thought of earlier people here needing to break the ice skimming the surface of water in birchbark pails. Stepping gingerly around both cats crouched at the end of the rug gang plank, lying in wait for the "food lady" to open a fresh can of wet food. The rain patting the roof, my feet padding, cats purring in anticipation and trees emerging in silhouette against the tip of dawn as I pull back the curtains. It's too early to think in full sentences.

Now, with the first gasp of steaming tea, I have returned to the red plaid bedding, lights off, to watch the sun brighten the world through the wet of falling rain. The growing distinctness of the visible world accompanies uneven spatters cascading across the roof. Swoops of wind shake rain off the trees in a sodden sweep. Inside, the white noise of the heater will work for three hours to raise the temperature to sixty. I've given it a little boost, turning on the oven to five hundred. It is so cold that I'm surprised not to see snow. The cats settle down with me, one curled into my arms as I manage to write around her; the other on top of my left foot.

Finally, the dawn reveals tree trunks first and then finer details like the lower branches of white pines against distant yellow leaves, salmon-colored fallen leaves upon plush moss, and the galvanized steel of the fire pit gleaming through the trees. This silver glint is echoed inside in the shiny aluminum tape with which I have covered the crack between the sliding windows. It holds back a little of the cold, a metallic sheen balancing the wood of the forest outside and the knotty-pine interior. The cabin's rustic walls seem at one with the forest trees, so close are the woods through the windows. The latter are themselves quite near, just two and a half feet from the foot of the bed and twelve inches on the right.

First frost has just occurred and with it the long winter commences, for spring comes late to northern Michigan. Tomorrow, the colony's water is being turned off. I have been reluctant to leave the cottage until that happens, but it is now time to migrate to my parents' winterized house.

Last week, when I drove Hollis to his grandparents after breakfast, we were startled by the sight of two sandhill cranes standing shoulder to shoulder in a field facing us as we drove by. I've seen cranes before in Michigan, but their rare beauty always draws a hushed exclamation and a caught breath. Never, however, have I seen cranes so near the roadside, simply looking down the pavement as if in expectation of us.

With their graceful necks and long legs, cranes are symbolic birds in many cultures. Because of their monogamy and longevity, encountering a pair like this suggests love and a long life. Across the globe, the courtship rituals and play of these majestic birds lead to associations with dance (Chadd and Taylor 34-8). For the Ojibwe people, writes linguist Basil Johnston of the Chippewas of Nawash Unceded First Nation in Ontario, the rarely heard call of the crane, along with its unusual vocal qualities, led its totem to be associated with leadership, where speech occurs only occasionally. This reticent verbalization ensures that others listen when the chief speaks; it also places persuasion at the heart of leadership (61). Eloquence thus characterizes the expression that inspires respectful attention and also the charisma that quietly draws respect because it is linked to integrity.

For me, the two cranes mean all of the above and more. Appearing in the frosty field, standing still together, they are at peace with themselves and one another in the clear morning. It reminds me of heart health. Love, in this sense, is not the passionate *sturm und drang* (storm and stress) of Western culture, the prankster emotion that can lead people to turn their lives (and those of their children) upside down. It is no accident that Cupid and Venus together stand for love. Stories involving this impish child and the voluptuous temptress reflect our cultural orientation; they influence the ways in which we interpret and act upon our emotions.

How different from the philosophy found in the *Tao Te Ching*. This central teaching of Taoism returns repeatedly to the need to control desires, as seen here:

Riding and hunting
Make his mind go wild with excitement;
Goods hard to come by
Serve to hinder his progress. (XII, 28)

To "progress" in life, moderation should replace over-excitement and greed. Maciocia similarly discusses how strong love or jealousy is understood to over-stimulate the *shen* of the heart in acupuncture. The foundation of health according to the three ancient Chinese philosophies of Confucianism, Taoism and Buddhism is in peaceful emotions.

How does this perception work in the West where we teach our children that nothing is more powerful than love? Our choices in romance and vocation are based on finding what we adore. In speaking about these choices as finding our passion, however, we step beyond calm and into the type of love that incites jealousy. To my way of thinking, this heart-sickness drives our whole culture.

Our stories affirm and recast our cultural ideologies. As autobiography theorist Carolyn Heilbrun summarizes, "it is a hard thing to make up stories to live by. We can only retell and live by the stories we have read or heard. We live our lives through texts ... they are what we must use to make new fictions, new narratives" (37). The rise of the novel is a case in point. Literary scholars understand two very different types of novels as the first long fictional works in English: Daniel Defoe's consideration of social construction in *Robinson Crusoe* (1719) and Samuel Richardson's hugely popular marriage-plot novel, *Pamela* (1740), based on love instead of family alliance. *Robinson Crusoe*'s shipwrecked titular character has some obvious points of synergy with my own consideration of the individual in the wild. In contrast, *Pamela*'s plot pivots around a servant girl who resists her employer's passionate advances until he finally proposes. The first half of Richardson's novel comprises the attempted seductions and the eventual marriage, while the second half is an etiquette guide. *Pamela* thereby balances emotional excess and suspenseful titillation with instruction on genteel morality and manners.

Today, we frequently encounter in television series and films the familiar marriage plot formula that drives suspense. Of course, we enjoy entertainment (I particularly love a good novel or opera), but in so doing it is simultaneously useful to realize the history and form of literary structures. In studying the genre of tragedy at Cambridge, for example, we approached the topic by differentiating between what we call a tragedy in real life and the literary techniques that create the genre of tragedy. In Greek or Shakespearian tragedy, some version of the expression "it is too late" frequently appears after a protagonist comes fully to realize the error of an earlier decision, often caused by hubris. A newspaper would not make a similar statement in reporting on a tragic death. The repeated formula, "it is too late," is a literary convention.

Preexisting ways of understanding our world repeated in popular media are not the only options for how we think and behave. Recognizing and understanding literary structure gives us the tools both to enjoy a story and also to select which texts will inspire our life choices. We might even decide to reshape a prevalent cultural narrative such as the love plot.

In considering the Chinese view of the psyche, Maciocia explains that emotion is understood as causing disease. He mentions an acupuncture point associated with ethical decisions or the choices made by an individual in relation to other people. This point, in calming anxiety, has a physical correlation in opening the chest and thus treating the heart. The Chinese character for *shen* is the heart specifically, but also the whole spirit, or the combined energies of the heart, kidney, spleen, lungs and liver. The *shen* of the heart must therefore always be treated alongside the other energies.

When I think of calming literature, the haiku comes to mind, a Japanese form originating with Buddhist monks. For example, Matsuo Bashō's poem from 1686 communicates a pond so still that we are drawn to the sound of the water when a small creature disturbs its surface:

old pond—
    a frog jumps in,
        water's sound
furuike ya / kawazu tobikomu / mizu no oto (180, p 54)

This poem, translated by David Landis Barnhill, encapsulates the healthy *shen*: mostly calm, but balanced with a little motion, like the *yin-yang* symbol.

଄ଓ

In my journey toward health, it has been necessary to recover and revise how I understand my own past. I recently had the opportunity to relive a little of my high school experience when Interlochen Arts Academy (IAA) held its 2020 alumni weekend online, making it possible for me to attend some of the events. The virtual coffee house made the greatest impact on me.

When I was a student, we had several coffee houses each year in the Fine Arts building. This stone structure has a little interior balcony overlooking the stage and main floor. Choir rehearsed here during the weekdays and films were shown on Saturday evenings. The interior managed to be simultaneously open and intimate, especially on a snowy night when the cold dark contrasted with the warmth of camaraderie inside. Under the light touch of a comedic master of ceremonies, we all let down our hair. Friends crooned pop songs, offered dramatic monologues, read their poems and performed choreographed dance.

The virtual coffeehouse was multi-generational, with alumni performers from the 1970s to 2020. The audience comprised students from as early as the 1960s, when IAA was founded. The chat box erupted in continuous enthusiasm and praise that radiated through the mid-October cold, the physical isolation and the technology.

This visceral reminder of the healthy luminosity of our high school experiences has led me to rethink my adolescence. My parents describe my start of ninth grade at IAA as a blossoming. To me, it was a relief from the public junior high where I had felt uncomfortable, except for when I was with a group of friends from orchestra. As I turned fourteen at Interlochen, however, daily experiences became sharper, like the forest coming into focus with the dawn. I seemed to awake with the positive energy that rebounded among students. We encouraged each other and applauded achievements of emotive artistry. In this isolated artist enclave in the Michigan woods, most of us felt that we finally belonged.

In our high school for the fine and performing arts, each student had an area of concentration and also had the opportunity to explore the other arts. Multiple performances, readings and exhibits by students, faculty and guests occurred every weekend in music, dance, drama, visual arts and creative writing. As practitioners, too, we attempted to create in new ways. Many of us replaced the two years of required physical education with dance, for instance. For me, this was a growth experience, for I knew nothing of ballet and was truly bewildered in my first weeks. The other students already knew the rudiments, while I, standing at the bar, had to learn the movements and their names by following along: "First position, *tendu, tendu, tendu.*" As winter set in, I became comfortable with the French terms. I wasn't very good, but I loved learning ballet and, in the second year, modern dance.

Our dance class was held in a window-lined studio on the shore of Green Lake, or Wahbekanetta. As we *pliéd* at the bar and *chasséd* across the room to Dave's improvisations at the upright piano, we absorbed the peace of "Water Lingers Again": watching the waves, the light, and the barn swallows nesting in the eaves and swooping over the water. The creative spirits of the world and humanity seemed united.

In a sense, we students concentrated on learning new skills in being. We discovered that "being" is itself creative during long walks alone or with friends on the wooded campus straddling the shores of Green and Duck Lakes. In warmer weather, music wafted through the pine trees from open windows in practice rooms and rehearsal spaces. Here was the natural world (creation) and our artistic expression, together.

Class voice lessons, another exploratory experience, led to something more serious for me. Having grown up in a musical family, I had learned to read music at age four, began piano lessons two years later, and added viola three years after that. Every evening, I practiced a half hour on each instrument to the accompaniment of "I can't hear you" from my parents when I got distracted. I was also in two orchestras – at school and in a community youth group – and in a regional youth choir.

All that enforced practice changed with the singing class at IAA. I had discovered my passion and I loved to practice. In the second semester of my freshman year, I accepted the invitation to move to private lessons and to declare a voice major. My vocal training went on for nine years, including at Oberlin Conservatory of Music. While I continued to love voice, the primal joy of those earliest years was gradually replaced by an attention to craft. My singing was probably most joyous while my training was beginning in the northern woods.

One of the most memorable experiences of that freshman year was hearing Leontyne Price in what was then considered her farewell tour. The academy transported its voice majors two hours south by bus to Grand Rapids to hear Price's extraordinary performance. Since then, I have heard many great singers and always had an embodied response. My zygomatic arch raises sympathetically as if my body sings silently even while assessing the singer's technique. But when I heard Leontyne Price, I was fourteen years old and new to singing. Instead of a physical mirroring in the concert hall, I hugged the exultation to myself all the way home until we walked off the bus as Interlochen. Then in the cold spring night, stars and moon overhead, I sang aloud in pure joy.

Although Walt Whitman was as yet only a name to me when I heard the great diva, my post-concert singing now reminds me of *Song of Myself*, Section 52:

> I too am not a bit tamed, I too am untranslatable,
> I sound my barbaric yawp over the roofs of the world.
>
> The last scud of day holds back for me,
> It flings my likeness after the rest and true as any on the shadow'd
>   wilds,
> It coaxes me to the vapor and the dusk.
>
> I depart as air, I shake my white locks at the runaway sun,
> I effuse my flesh in eddies, and drift it in lacy jags.
>
> I bequeath myself to the dirt to grow from the grass I love,
> If you want me again look for me under your boot-soles.

You will hardly know who I am or what I mean,
But I shall be good health to you nevertheless,
And filter and fiber your blood. (1332–43)

Knowing that Whitman was an opera afficionado, I wonder if that "barbaric yawp" was more musical than suggested by the onomatopoeia. My singing experience that night in 1983 was likewise a melodic "flinging" as "true" as the "spotted hawk" (1331) with which Whitman begins the final section of his long poem. The untranslatable sound of glory is as elemental as "the vapor and the dusk," transported by atmosphere and song ("air"), embodied in "lacy jags" of sonority that vibrate through solid surfaces, yet also planted firmly in the dirt and blades of grass underfoot. This song (mine and Whitman's poem) is the message of "good health": it is heart-song.

The flying hawk's meaning in Whitman's poem differs from that of the standing pair of cranes with which I began this chapter; the yawp's bodily fling is the opposite of inner silence. There is more than one kind of love. Thus the Vietnamese Buddhist monk, Thích Nhất Hạnh suggests that our first love is not what we think it is:

Think about your first love, how it came about, where it took place, what brought you to that moment. Recall the details of the experience and look at them calmly and deeply, with compassion and understanding. You will discover things that you did not notice the first time. You will discover that your "first love" was not really the first. Many streams nourish and support the river of your life. (79)

When I read this soon after it was published in 1995, I thought back to my first crush on a boy and then cast my mind back before that. Was there an earlier love?

Following the trail back, my thoughts landed on an experience in first grade. It was not dissimilar to what happened when we had the privilege of hearing Leontyne Price just eight years later. In elementary school, the whole class had been bussed to Traverse City High School to see a musical. The name of the show has long since sunk away, if indeed I retained it past the day itself. What has endured is my response. On the way home afterwards, I sat at the back of the yellow school bus. Seeking privacy, I heard the songs from the show again in my inner ear, for the music had transported me. It was an experience of exhilaration that would recur again and again when I heard particularly powerful music.

What struck me most during the reunion's virtual coffee house was not the level of performance (although it was excellent), but rather the type of response that it elicited in the chat box. There was such warmth of support for every performer. It was a step back in time to our daily teen experience of a positive energy that ricocheted from one person to the next. There was no quota of excellence. Rather, a community supported each person to achieve his or her best, and applauded individual and collective achievement. If you were unable to achieve first chair in the orchestra or the lead in the play, well, it was up to you to take the responsibility to return to the practice room and your teacher.

Artistic training on this level requires individuals to search inside for deep truths. Such a process teaches lessons of resiliency and sympathy. My fellow alumni expressed that the latter naturally emerged from being asked to interpret musical compositions and dramatic roles. In the humanities classrooms, too, we often approached history and literature from the perspective of the ideas that would help to shape us. Our academic teachers were excellent role models. Their generosity of spirit impressed me and I filled the margins of my notebooks with their wise insights. They offered deep personal integrity to us and I likewise felt truly seen for myself at Interlochen. This desire for communal insight into and acceptance of the individual persists for me, much like the cranes standing silently at the roadside, waiting quietly to be seen. We probably all want to be seen like this.

What I thought I was learning at Interlochen – excellence in the arts – turns out to be a sort of luminous heart health, of joy in human communication and mutual well-being, balanced with the calm of the natural environment. In after years, some Interlochen students did indeed make careers as artists, whether as practitioners or teachers. Most of us found other professional trajectories that still revealed the stamp of our Interlochen education. In my cohort, there are numerous educators (including in non-arts areas) and healers, whether in therapy, medicine or holistic health. These professions are motivated by the heart: by love for others and the desire to reach out to improve quality of life, just as the arts can do.

Not dissimilarly, Maciocia speaks of the need for the *zhi* of the kidneys to give structure to our mental and emotional life. The intention to have a calm joy as the basis of our loving relationships makes "to love" a verb as well as a feeling. Another way of understanding this concept is that the *zhi* (a water element) and the *shen* of the heart (fire) balance each other. When there is too much fire (without water or calm), it can lead to an excessive joy. Thinking back to the performances at IAA, the exuberance of a performance was balanced with the Michigan weather – a cold fall, winter and spring through which we walked, skipped and ran to the venue and back again.

Similarly, my husband and I take turns holding the space for each other so that we are mutually supported in having careers that make us happy as individuals. This has included my financially supporting the family during the period of Bruce's retraining and entry into the profession in which he now thrives, and then Bruce's calm assumption of things around the house during a period of particular overwork for me. Acting in loving ways supports each other's health for it offers a stable, peaceful base rather than contributing to the stress that can manifest disease. In fact, somehow despite our family's separation from each other during the pandemic, Bruce and I have only become stronger. Hollis and I have really needed Bruce during our illnesses, and he has been our rock. We only miss him more as autumn continues, while also knowing that we can and do stand on our own two feet.

This realization about what it means to love suggests that perhaps I needed to reach further back than first grade to find an earlier love. Before my six-year-old adoration of the high school musical, there was the love of my parents and the serenity of the universe. The *Tao Te Ching* puts it like this: "Returning to one's roots is known as stillness. / This is what is meant by returning to one's destiny" (XVI, 37). We studied this passage at IAA with our teacher, Howard Hintze, in his literature course, "Man and Destiny." My annotations show that we discussed these lines as meaning returning to the source, the settling of pride and simplicity. For the next two lines, "Returning to one's destiny is known as the constant. / Knowledge of the constant is known as discernment" (37), our class conversation concerned the idea of natural activity. This type of innate order is cyclical, for the seeds planted in high school continue to mature, and they were there from before, too. We were not only making, but also returning to our destiny as we studied this ancient philosophy.

The passage that I cited earlier from Nhất Hạnh continues along the same lines:

Your first love has no beginning and no end; it is always in transformation. Your first love is still present, continuing to shape your life. When you are serene, smiling, and breathing mindfully, I am sure you will understand. (87)

Being calm is first love; this inner serenity is also a joyful state that allows the heart continually to renew and transform. The time that I have right now – writing in nature, feeling and reflecting on its peace – is first love.

While I walked today, I meditated on being calm, feeling the heart of the world and simply looking. Like the two cranes, true love is synonymous with peace.

I observed that the shoulder seasons of autumn and spring share dramatic, daily changes in plant life – more visible than in winter and summer. The forest floor was bright with red and gold leaves, and through the long grey trunks reaching up, and the loden cedar branches drooping down, the lake glimmered blue-grey, like the overcast sky. As my path took me away from the lake, the bare branches of hardwoods obscured the water with a hazy plum smudge, against which yellow leaves and green conifers seemed brighter. As autumn hangs on tenaciously for a few more days, the yellow trees and brittle ferns appear predominantly jaundiced and decaying, with the relief of pink-red maple leaves overhead and crimson sumac blazing in the shrubbery at welcome intervals. Now, I long for the sparkle of new snow that I know is not far off.

Yet as much as I look forward to the next season, I am also content, here and now. Like the two cranes, shoulder-to-shoulder, waiting for the red car with mother and child approaching out of browning fields and crimson trees. No – not waiting, but simply being at peace inside and with each other. They, and we, return to our roots, a motion forward, backward and present, all at once. In that aspiration is movement and stillness:

I do my utmost to attain emptiness;
I hold firmly to stillness (Tzu, XVI, 37)

This is a healthy human heart and spirit, individually and with a partner who similarly aspires so that it can be achieved together.

HE term "dry cabin" refers to a dwelling without running water. I learned this last night as I was looking at the online reviews for a camping commode, liners and coconut coir, such as composting toilets use. It's the third week of October and yesterday at noon the colony's shared well was turned off in preparation for winter. Our electricity remains on and the cottage has both an efficient wall heater and a new space heater, although we rarely use the latter. When I first rise in the morning, I can see my breath. Outside, frost decorates the windshield of my car.

Staying in the cottage into the snowy season was not the plan. I tried to move from here to my parents' four-season house a couple nights ago. Hollis had already made the transition a few days before so that I could pack and clean uninterrupted. I accordingly loaded up the car and drove the cats and my things to Mom and Dad's, where I was to stay in an *en suite* on the lower level.

When it came time to make the move, however, I found that I wasn't ready to leave the woods. At dinner in the winterized house, the central heat dried my throat to soreness and I was too warm. More to the point, I'd gone a bit wild in a way that was beyond language. Still, a poor night's sleep surprised me given my exhaustion from cleaning and packing while still unwell. With only four hours of sleep, I started the day groggy and ill. In contrast, my sleep at the cottage was deep, restful and eight to ten hours long.

I couldn't adequately explain to my parents or myself what led me to return to the cottage. In a further departure from my usual life, I am not even going to try. It doesn't have to make rational sense to be the right course. I had already been planning to breakfast at the cottage and spend my days there. Now I would stay in the woods full-time except for evenings with the family, including dinner, spending time with Hollis and having a shower. This was what I'd already planned, with the exception of where I would sleep, and the schedule was easy to articulate. What was impossible to communicate was the removal with the cats to the cottage for sleep.

Immediately apparent, too, was that I couldn't subject Hollis to what would be a shivery experience. He had already complained all summer about the cold toilet seat in the cottage. It was unquestionably chilly now with the heat turned down to forty-five degrees Fahrenheit at night and sixty during the day (seven and sixteen Celsius). I gave him the choice and he was happy to stay with his grandparents; his journey does not need to align with mine in this instance. As it turned out, Hollis and Bruce would sometimes visit the cottage during the day or at night, but these stays were infrequent. It felt undeniably odd making this arrangement, but we all agreed to do whatever it took to support my getting better. What I needed was healing, long slumber and to wake in tune with the natural world, including its cold.

With mutterings about the trees and needing deep sleep, circadian rhythms and the unconscious place that I could reach by being so close to nature, I packed up my red Volkswagen Beetle and opened the moonroof. I heard echoes of Thoreau in my head as Mom and Dad waved me off with trust if incomprehension, saying that they hoped I would return with the cats in the event of a snowstorm.

Then out of the subdivision, along fallow fields, across the highway, through hilly pastures with wooden fences and into the woods. Finally, I was back to the cottage, greeted by fluttering leaves. Simply being in this space dissolved the weary illness that I had felt since waking. With the water being turned off that day, I realized that wellness does not depend upon having a functioning well.

I thought again of Thoreau's experiment to live deliberately in the small cabin that he built overlooking Walden Pond. He narrated this experiment in what has become a classic of American literature. *Walden* was published in 1854, he says, as a response to the curiosity of his neighbors. I like to imagine these friends and relations satiating their curiosity over dinner table conversation with their transcendental friend, whom they regularly fed out of concern that he was going hungry. Surely, rows of beans would not provide enough to fill a man's stomach, they must have declared among themselves. Thoreau had a ready response:

> One farmer says to me, "You cannot live on vegetable food solely, for it furnishes nothing to make bones with;" and so he religiously devotes a part of his day to supplying his system with the raw material of bones; walking all the while he talks behind his oxen, which, with vegetable-made bones, jerk him and his lumbering plow along (204)

No doubt, Thoreau was glad to vary his diet and his solitude by striding through second-growth forests and fields to Concord, Massachusetts (for the forests, see Journal 156, 160). It would have taken him as long to walk the mile's distance as it takes me to drive from the cottage to my parents' house for similar meals and conversation, a shower and the washing machine. Just a twenty-minute journey to a suburban world and then back, retracing the way under a northern sky free of light pollution, into the deep, dark woods – perfect Gruffalo territory, we tease our son.

When I first realized while writing my English honors thesis at Oberlin College that Thoreau's social isolation was not quite as remote as his subject, I was disappointed because this naturalist's experience had seemed as raw as the land that he settled. He had built his cabin motivated by individual desire and then structured *Walden* in response to community members who questioned his sustainable lifestyle. Surely when he nipped into Concord for a chat over dinner with friends like poet William Ellery Channing and philosopher Ralph Waldo Emerson, the conversation would have been more supportive. Among this cohort, the fact that Thoreau made and wrote about radical lifestyle choices was not that unusual. Emerson was Thoreau's landlord at Walden and Ellery Channing had been the one to encourage Thoreau to "build yourself a hut, & there begin the grand process of devouring yourself alive." For Ellery Channing, the dining is made into the process itself. "I see no alternative, no other hope for you. Eat yourself up; you will eat nobody else, nor anything else."

The idea of mastication seems to have stuck with Thoreau, for he formulated his theory of existence thus:

> I went to the woods because I wished to live deliberately, to front only the essential facts of life, and see if I could not learn what it had to teach, and not, when I came to die, discover that I had not lived ... I wanted to live deep and suck out all the marrow of life, ... to drive life into a corner, and reduce it to its lowest terms (271)

While the first sentence is often quoted, it is useful to remember that Thoreau metaphorically understood "Where I Lived, and What I Lived for," as he titled the chapter, as a sucking of life's vitality, or the marrow from its bones. Rather than devouring himself as Ellery Channing would have, or being too weak from vegetable-made bones, Thoreau would imbibe life at its most vital and thereby discover its essence.

Part of paring down to bare bones is to make food, clothing and shelter simple so that the life of the mind can thrive. "Our life is frittered away by detail," Thoreau continues in the next paragraph. "Simplicity, simplicity, simplicity! I say, let your affairs be as two or three, and not a hundred or a thousand" (271). Besides tilling his fields and walking the woods, Thoreau wrote while at Walden. Conversation among transcendental Concord would have furthered this emphasis on the mind in nature, or thinking as forming what existence is. This orientation, including its non-doctrinal spirituality, has much in common with my own holistic process.

What I had not realized until I began to live in my own dry cabin was that homecooked meals in comfortable houses with dear people do not negate the experience of living deliberately in a woodland cottage above a lake. The reason that I live in my own wooden hut is that here I can be deeply connected to the earth, its seasons and its living things. This lifestyle is healing. Visiting Mom and Dad's insulated home feels like the unusual thing to me now. I spend a short enough period there; it's not too tiring nor does it sever my connectedness to the land. Rather, these evenings allow me to be a parent and daughter, for us to spend time together and for me to luxuriate in a hot shower. My gratitude for family and my appreciation of running water are both greater now. Water has become so precious that I value it more, just as I cherish our family time because I am gaining energy and health for it through an immersive communion with nature.

By nature, I mean my own as well as the earth's. Indeed, the two seem closer to one. When I wake early, under a clear sky, the quiet and the night are so deep and I am so warm beneath two duvets, that it is more womb-like than anything that I consciously remember. It resonates with primal memory. Without the hum of the hot water heater intermittently kicking in, the thick silence of night wraps around me. Comforting. Cushioning. Can anyone doubt the profundity of this healing state? For this, I remain in the cottage off-season.

Like the northern woods, waters and wild creatures that have offered lessons as we experience life in close proximity to each other, there is something to learn by living in a dry cabin. Luckily, I enjoy hiking and tent camping in the backwoods, so the routine is not entirely new. I am not fully off grid, moreover, but rather am interdependent. It would be impossible to survive the northern winter without a source of heat and there is neither a fireplace nor a wood-burning stove at the cottage. Electricity in the cottage, and easy access to a shower and washing machine at Mom and Dad's, makes it possible for me to heal, to stay safe and to enjoy my time in the cottage rather than, for example, risking reinfection at public laundromats.

I am living simply, not experimenting with extremity. The lack of running water was something that seemed manageable, rather than being my motivation. A shiny four-gallon red bucket with a lid and a spigot sits on the side of the kitchen sink to provide water for handwashing and dishes. Conserving water begins immediately when the available amount is visible in this bucket and the plastic bottles that I refill at Polly's house or my parents' place. Polly, whose winterized house has its own well, has kindly offered me the use of her facilities now that she has migrated to her California home for the winter. As I look around at the gallon jugs of water lining the shelf, I realize with amusement that here, again, is water lingering.

A dry cabin requires mindfulness when the water that you have is what you carry in. Quickly, it becomes apparent how much water is wasted when it appears easily at the turn of a tap. I knew this logically, but now it is a physical necessity to conserve. My mind boggles at attempting to conceive how much water is wasted worldwide during teeth-brushing alone. *The San Diego Union-Tribune* reports in an article called "Tap Water Can Add Up to Big Waste" that "about two gallons of water flow from a faucet each minute. Something as simple as turning off the water while brushing your teeth can save up to three or four gallons of water per person per day." I contrast this with my pretty Bonne Maman jam jar of water sitting on the bathroom sink, from which I have enough water to brush my teeth two or three times. I go through about two gallons a day for all of my needs at the cottage.

Mindfulness in a dry cabin includes the lesson of patience; it takes time to heat water. We use a kettle on the stovetop for boiling larger quantities than a mug in the microwave. I'm used to the pleasurable anticipation every morning of waiting for the first hint of the whistle in order to rescue the kettle, pour the boiling water and wait a few minutes for a strong cup of tea. With the kettle filled just enough for a mug or two, it's only a short wait. However, heating the entire kettle for dishwashing – that takes forethought.

In such a rural location, some aspects of mindfulness are simple facts of life. When I was a child, there were no local toy stores. The Sears *Wish Book* would arrive in September in advance of the Christmas season and my brother and I would pour over the pages, dog-earing those with our choices for Santa. My parents placed the order early enough for Christmas delivery and we were never disappointed by presents not arriving in time. The Traverse City area has grown a lot since the 1970s, and there are now many brick-and-mortar stores, but the cottage is still a thirty- to forty-five-minute drive away. If possible, we make only one trip weekly to accomplish all errands, including grocery shopping and filling the tank at the cheapest pump for miles around. I grew up planning in order to avoid wasting money, time and disappointment. In a dry cabin, however, living deliberately with forethought and patience is taken to a new level.

Similarly, the lack of insulation has been acceptable so that I can continue in the woods. In comparison to winter camping, I have many luxuries, including a furnace. The unexpected advantages have been numerous, including deep sleep and, therefore, increased physical healing and access to the unconscious mind. Nature is closer, too, without insulation. For practical reasons of expense and conservation,

I keep the thermostat low. In doing so, my body temperature is synched to the external world. It suffers fewer shocks from transitioning between inside and outside. Not only does the house lack toxic insulation, but the hairline cracks mean that healthy aerosols from the surrounding forest find their way inside more readily, even off-season when the windows are shut. The temperature does not feel cold to me because I have adjusted gradually along with the external world.

The cats know how to conserve heat. Whether I'm writing in my notebook or sleeping, one or both Ragamuffins curl up tight against me, to mutual advantage. It reminds me of the winter dens of chipmunks that Till regularly finds on our walks together. Unlike most house cats, when I put Till in his vest for walking, he takes off at a good clip and walks with me like a puppy. He also periodically verges off the mossy paths and dirt roads to jump at chipmunks as they reflexively leap down holes. Several times, he has investigated old stumps, clad in tufts of grass and fuzzy with moss. Upon peering closer, I see a broken bit at the top of the stump where some creature has gnawed an entrance and, off to the side, another hole dug into a mound of moss or just visible under fallen leaves. These chipmunk-sized round doors probably lead to a cozy den where little honey-striped companions snuggle, a gently-breathing ball of fur, with store rooms for acorns off to the side. It is not that far off from our own snugged group, breathing co-regulating, with Till's soft snores bringing the laugh lines to the corners of my eyes in a wonder that seeks not to disturb by audible expression. These creature comforts are so simple and yet profound, with a warmth emanating from mutual reliance, trust and love.

In heating our houses as much as most of us do in the winter, even our pets lose nature's rhythms since there is no need to group together in warmth. Part of what drives the isolation of modern individuality (living apart from the earth and each other) is the desire to be more comfortable and regulated, while still economizing through insulation and energy-efficient appliances. I understand. In one sense, I would like to insulate the cottage to better conserve electricity and my wallet, but I have neither the budget nor the desire to destroy the original look of our historic cottage. It is usually just for summer anyway.

It is because of living in the dwelling as it is that I am newly aware of something lacking in materialist culture. What I crave is adjusting with an instantaneous fine-tuning as I live in my now-dry cottage. For the warmth that I have, including the cats, I am profoundly grateful. I feel likewise for the roof keeping me dry on a near-freezing night when the rain sounds on the roof. I appreciate electricity, light and the water that I provide. My very life appears to be a thanksgiving for the time to be here, residing thus with wildlife and the beauty of the world. Living deliberately because you have less, causes you to feel more. At root, that emotion is gratitude.

Ironically, I have COVID to thank for this new awareness. I did, of course, feel fortunate to survive the virus, but the recovery has included many difficult days. It is tiring and discouraging to feel unwell for so long, and deeply frustrating not to be able to work. The type of gratitude for having survived is so different from the gratitude of living deliberately that it should be called by a different word. How can this way of being be shared if we lack the language to conceptualize it?

Even minimalism is different from my experience, although it comes close. The minimalist lifestyle and design approach pares down to essentials, including in household furnishings and the size of one's wardrobe. Decluttering means a cleaner look to homes and this in turn provides relief from the incessant capitalist hum of "more, more, buy more."

Minimalists find happiness in what they have rather than in what they want, and they go about living on the grid as they always have done. Their focus is not necessarily on conserving natural resources, but rather on fewer commodities and clean architectural design lines. Minimalists pare down, but by saying that they are not consumerists they are, ironically, defined by it. They are *not* consumerists, rather than being something else for its own sake.

In my need to live here, in contrast, even if the cottage is dry, the lessons of mindfulness have felt like gifts from nature. They arise because of my decision to be close to and within nature's embrace. That decision feels more symbiotic than if I had intended only mindfulness. When life presents a delightful surprise, it elicits a particularly potent level of gratitude: it feels good spontaneously to be given to and to receive. We thus know the character of the divine and of the earth as benevolent and caring.

The awareness of being given to inspires reciprocity. Automatically, I find myself giving back through the very medium of the message: water conservation. Dry cabins offer lessons by the simple desire to be one with natural rhythms. Not minding the lack of running water, ironically, builds the mindfulness. This is a different system of exchange from minimalism; rather than being about individual fulfillment through turning away from consumerism, it's about mutual healing through relating with nature. Take only what you need, be thankful and give back. Sustainability emphasizes this nest of ideas without necessarily including the benefit to human health.

Naturopathic medicine, however, is founded on the idea that living in concert with nature has a positive biological impact on people along with the ecosystem. After a couple of days in the now-dry cottage, the weather suddenly cools and my metabolism ratchets up. Burning more calories and feeling hungrier is a relief after the metabolic slowdown of my initial battle with COVID-19 when I was bedridden in the spring.

Now, I am losing the resulting weight and have more energy. Last week, I could just barely manage a twenty-minute walk. Great fatigue set in that evening, but the next day I was better. This was an improvement over the last three months when this exertion would cause post-exertional malaise for the ensuing four or five days. Previous to that, I was only managing to walk – slowly – around a city block every two or three days during the spring. But now after two days in the dry cabin, my circadian rhythm aligns with seasonal changes and the quiet, and I can walk thirty minutes at my usual fast pace without any onset of nausea or fatigue. I can't do it daily, but it's still a significant and sudden improvement in health. What a relief.

My senses are rejuvenating, too, in a manner that I had not realized that they needed. Because most of my time is spent in the cottage or outdoors, my soundscape comprises the natural world. I don't have appliances or technology that hum and bleat. There's only the gruff static of the furnace when it kicks on, the warning screech of the kettle and the occasional beep of the microwave or toaster oven. The voices are my own, singing or calling to the cats, or their little mews to me. My favorite sonority is the vibrating purr of feline happiness, especially when Till sees the harness in my hands and loudly expresses his anticipatory pleasure. The most jarring noise is when my cell phone erupts in insistent, demanding ring tones. When I enter my parents' home now (by no means a loud environment by most standards) its sensory overload exhausts me. I love evenings with my family and then I return to my woodland dwelling to find peace and energy on the doorstep, offering warm welcome as I step over the threshold. Being sensorially overwhelmed in a modern dwelling was probably the main reason that I returned to the cottage. I needed to live more simply, like Thoreau.

The woods do not feel so dry this morning with the external world dripping, splattering, trickling with last night's deluge. My rain bucket outside the front door collected almost a gallon of water overnight. I don't know to what use I'll put it, but it will not go to hair washing. Like my mother, I draw the line there. As part of the conversation during our ancestors' dinner, Mom shared how as a child visiting her paternal aunts, she found it strange to wash her hair in rain water. They told her that it was soft water, special for her hair. Aunts Evadne and Esther had learned this practice as children in New Mexico where water was scarce. When their father moved the family to Oberlin, the whole family must have thought daily about water conservation, too, for my great-grandfather's occupation was to manage the city's waterworks.

As an Oberlin undergraduate, I used to walk with my friends to the "res" (reservoir): a system of two ponds separated by a bank. We walked the path on this bank to reach a wooded area for picnics and rambling. I always thought of my ancestors as I walked between yet another set of twinned waters (albeit ponds, not lakes like Interlochen) and looked curiously at the stone turret that surely contained original machinery for the waterworks. I did not know then to trace the waterways of family memory further back to conserving New Mexico rain for clean hair. I bet my great-aunts Evadne and Esther did, however. Now, having been told how water conservation flows through the family veins, I set out a bucket as it began to storm last night.

Maybe this five and a half inches of collected water will go to flush the toilet. The colony water is turned off, but the cottage's pipes won't be winterized for a couple of days yet. At that point, a loud machine sucks the remaining water out of the pipes and we pour anti-freeze down the drains of the washing machine, cast iron bathtub, toilet and dishwasher. Because I yet remain in the cottage, the sinks will stay in use until I finally leave, pouring anti-freeze down the drains as I depart in advance of the coldest months.

During the few days before the toilet is prepared for winter, I can flush it by pouring water into the back. I'm appalled to realize that it takes at least two and a half gallons to accomplish this task. Sometimes I take advantage of Polly's generous offer of her home with its running water, but I also prepare for late nights, early mornings and storms when I don't fancy stepping outside just to use the toilet at her place. It is cold and the coyotes and black bear make me cautious about being outside in the dark, alone except for the trees reaching up their long sinewy arms to the moon shining large overhead and the sky salted with stars.

Being a scholar of Victorian literature, I naturally begin my online quest for the solution by entering the word "chamber pot" into the search engine. I discover online that today's term is "camping commode." Furthermore, the collapsible type is a popular COVID accessory: stay safe on cross-country road trips by peeing into a bucket. Looking ahead, it may come in handy for post-pandemic camping trips. Amazon Prime would deliver in two days and I would be all set for my back country living.

Ha! Now the cats will have their litter box and I will have mine: Furs' and Hers.

ဆ၄ာ

The camping commode has arrived, including a black bag with prominent white lettering: "Portable Folding Toilet." So much for discretion. Undoubtedly, I would prefer indoor plumbing, but when compared to a late night trip down an unlit lane in freezing weather with lurking coyotes, this portable loo is just fine.

The cottage is now fully prepared for winter. The hoses from the back of the washing machine coil around to the front, propping the lid open. The toilet bowl is pink with antifreeze. I've taped down the lid with blue painter's tape so that no one accidentally uses it. Bathtub and dishwasher are also winterized and a bottle of antifreeze sits inside the bathroom vanity in anticipation of my exit before January. With surprise, I discover that the commode is preferable to fetching and then pouring gallons of water down the back of the toilet. The liners are sturdy and the coir nullifies odor.

A string of LED fairy lights on copper wire makes merry in the living room as darkness descends around 5:30 now. At this time of year, night lengthens past daylight for at least an hour and the festoons of light under the wooden cathedral ceiling make the darkness cheerful. The stinging of snow against dry leaves heralds winter and the world feels at peace in this cozy cabin with its festive lights.

The winter calm marks a change of pace that rural cultures have known for centuries before modern amenities made it possible to disregard the earth's rhythms. Certain stories are only told after the first frost in traditional Anishinaabek life as families gather inside for warmth. In farming communities, school occurs between harvest and sowing because the earth remains untended at this time. Families come together inside in the dark and cold of winter, around points of light.

At acupuncture today, Abigail felt my pulse and noticed a change in my body's rhythm.

"It's like a new chapter, isn't it?" I said.

"That's exactly what it's like. You're more regular. When you first came in here in August, your pulse was racing. This regularity has to do with the spleen. I'm really liking where it's at." The *yi* of the spleen connects to self-care in diet, sleep and exercise.

While the current chapter mostly discusses the mindful healing that arrives as part of the conservation of water in a dry cabin, underlying it is the Sleeping Bear. Preparing for winter, Makwa slows. Deep inside, I similarly feel the need to be in the forest. While we always feel the benefits of forest bathing, I have never felt it so strongly before. Perhaps I was simply ready to tap into this vast source of nature's energy, as Abigail put it. Even though humanity has diminished the earth through various abuses, its energy is still here, massive and ready with enormous restorative potential. It simply requires that we reach out to it and offer something back, such as conservation.

HIS morning, a persistent bird-like chirp interrupted my journaling. Both cats were sleeping soundly on the couch and the world was at peace except for this insistent cheep—cheep—cheep—cheep—cheep. After five minutes, I padded over in my wooly socks to see what my avian friend was up to. Following the sound to the front deck, I found an eastern *chipmunk* on the top step looking directly at me, frozen in place and rapidly chirping. Our gazes locked, I wondered what my little neighbor wanted to tell me.

We see chipmunks daily, but never has one stared at the house – and me - emitting this urgent, continuous sound. In another minute or two, she turned sideways and continued clucking for two or three more minutes, brown furry sides and cheeks slightly rippling.

After she stopped and agilely jumped down the steps and away, I looked up the sound on a National Geographic website to learn that this rapid clucking was the warning sound for an aerial predator. Chipping with its interspersed pauses between vocalizations, however, communicated terrestrial threat. Chipmunk was alerting all her sisters, cousins and aunts to stay in their underground dens until danger had passed. She sounded the alarm for me and the cats from whom she usually scurried, too, for it seemed likely that she was the chipmunk who lived under the cottage and after whom Till liked to lunge, his harness pulling him up short.

I cannot help but think about this neighborly message as a communication that called for my greater attention. It alerted me to the need to interpret an earnest vocalization that I did not understand. This was a complex symbol, for it also pointed to what was perceived beyond the hearing: to the unseen, silent presence of the raptor who revealed itself to the chipmunk, probably while flying overhead. So I needed to think about epistemology, or how I make meaning regarding both what I can empirically perceive (the chipmunk) and that which I cannot (the bird).

What am I justified in believing about the unseen predator? I know that hawks and owls are the birds that normally pose an aerial threat for chipmunks. Owls can be ruled out since they are nocturnal and it was 10 a.m. Hawks line the highways in this part of Michigan, but I'd never seen them in our woods. Bald eagle? Bald eagles will sometimes eat the small double-striped creatures, although these raptorial birds prefer fish. It would be unusual, but within the colony there had been a sighting in August and then again about a month ago, in late September. On both occasions, the eagle was in flight.

The more memorable event occurred this summer before my leave began. A neighbor was outside on the balmy August evening when our black bear was spotted by Duchess, who barked enthusiastically. A little before that, "A fish fell out of the sky," as Wade tells it, and hit the roof of the log cabin near the lake stairs. Wade looked up and saw a bald eagle that had lost his grip on a freshly caught lake trout. The fish fell wriggling to the roof, slid down and landed, thump, on the ground. The circling bird did not dive to retrieve his dinner because of human presence and so the fish became, instead, supper in a frying pan.

It is amazing to think about how most of the wildlife in this wood remains hidden except for the alerts given by secondary agents. Thus Duchess barked and a trio of humans looked up from their conversation to see a black bear ambling down the middle of a dirt road. The fish fell from the sky and the magnificent bird of Jove revealed itself to the man below. Now, the chipmunk delivers its urgent message of an aerial threat: "There's a mighty feathered warrior nearby!" But I did not understand chipmunk enough at the time to look up from my little cheeping friend and search the skies. Now, I have learned and next time I will understand the distinctions among clucking, chipping and trilling, as scientists term the aerial, terrestrial and moving warnings voiced by the ubiquitous chipmunk.

For now, I focus on becoming more aware and learning a language that surrounds us in the north woods. The lesson of the moment comes from Chipmunk, who appeared at my front door and looked me in the eye and said ... something. Bear and coyote hadn't made that direct contact, nor had the many other wild animals that we see, with the possible exception of a doe who stands stationary, looking at me during my walks until my careful approach frightens her. Chipmunk, in contrast, included me in her warning; she made me an ally, unmoving when I approached. She seemed to think that I would understand as I stood blankly staring.

Abigail reminded me later that day that the woodland animals are likely to engage differently with me because they are not used to humans remaining in our summer enclave past first frost. Normally, the mice move in as the cottage is deserted and the weather cools. This year, our cats keep these tiny colonizers away. The wildlife is used to winter's darkness and quiet, not the car departing and arriving, lights shining through the trees. Cottage life may be a quieting for me, but the hum of the heater is unusual activity for them. No doubt, Abigail said, they will present themselves to me in ways other than they do in summer, when they are used to being scarce while humans occupy the colony and make a lot of noise flushing toilets.

With this in mind, perhaps Chipmunk viewed me as closer to its world. "Hey, sister, you who are still here with us, I need to warn you about the big bird."

We are together; I am included because of place. Sharing the same shelter, I provide warmth through my floor (their ceiling) and I keep the cats at bay on their leashes or inside. More than that, I am ready to tune in, perceive and reciprocate the gentle welcome and lack of judgement emanating from wild lives. This tender receptiveness reminds me that animals, like humans, respond to gentle openness.

CRRO

There can be a generous, community spirit in the wild. Now that my ears are open, I frequently hear the chipmunks' warnings as I walk outside with our grey kitty in a navy harness and our ginger tom looking like a cool dude in his blue bandana. Our silvery Ragamuffin behaves like most cats on a leash. She meanders, sits, pounces on a falling leaf, eats some grass and sits some more. Moss makes the softest cushion, if it's not soaked like a wet sponge from the night's rain. Mostly, I carry her these days, giving her some fresh air while she shivers slightly in my arms. She looks and looks as we lope along, her brother keeping pace at my heels or suddenly racing in front. Our orange cat behaves puppy-like, frisking and prancing, but he morphs smoothly into his feline self when a chipmunk appears. Then he is suddenly all cat, stealthily stalking or suddenly bounding as Chippy disappears down a hole or sits frozen on the stoop of a winterized cottage.

Now I hear chipmunk warnings all around me: the cluck of terrestrial threat repeated low with pauses. My little buddy is the perceived predator. I suppose that makes me an ally to squirrel's cousin as I hold the leash, ensuring that our cat remains unsuccessful in his hunting.

Back at the cottage, our chipmunk broadcasts aerial threats twice during the day from the deck, a frozen sentinel perched on a newel post cap. During the day, while I rock in the hammock, a constant chipping and trilling communicates ongoing vigilance on behalf of our energetic striped friends. It's exhausting to keep up with all these *communiqués*; it would drive me crazy to have messenger alerts beeping all day on my cell phone. Yet this is how our tiny forest friend survives the wild: by speaking and honoring a social agreement. Like the oral contract of traditional Anishinaabek culture, the speaker articulates an inner truth.

Thus Chipmunk lets everyone know about real threats; the lives of her friends and family depend upon heeding the vocalizations as true. When words can be trusted as bonds, then integrity and respect become the foundations of civic life.

Given this serious intent, it's interesting that the chipmunk commonly symbolizes joy, perhaps because of the cheer that he brings to us as we watch his scampering forays and bulging cheeks. Hollis and I smiled all summer at the chipmunk's dash as he leapt down holes and under summer cottages. In 1952, *The Saturday Evening Post* featured a poem by the American humorist, Ogden Nash, that nicely captures the complex spirit of Chipmunk's character:

> He moves with flickering indecision
> Like stripes across the television.
>
> ...
>
> Yet his ultimate purpose is obviously, very:
> To get back to his chipmonastery. (3–4, 7–8)

In the "flickering indecision" and ultimate monastical purpose, Nash captures the feeling of a scurry motivated, apparently, by timidity. "But the chipmunk is twice as shy as I" (2), the speaker prefaces his observations. The painful shyness attributed to the creature, however, contrasts with the sound of the poem: the lilt of lines that shift between duple and triple meter, the stress on the penultimate syllable (feminine rhymes) in the rhyming couplets, and the cleverness of the neologism, "chipmonastery."

I have suggested a more profound character in considering the sounds made by chipmunks as oriented toward concern for community welfare. Yet, upon reflection, chipmunks are not alone among animals in possessing this latter characteristic, whereas their headlong rush is distinctive. The chipmunk's name is even derived from its characteristic sprint. "One who descends trees headlong," the Ojibwe called him (ajidamoo), which became "Chipmunk" in English (Bright 10).

So-called civilized human culture seems more the exception than do chipmunk ways. While large numbers of people have flouted medical guidelines during a pandemic and have therefore contributed to preventable deaths and chronic illnesses, chipmunks *en masse* energetically stockpile food for winter, care for their young and transmit alerts for community survival. In fact, the chipmunk takes responsibility beyond its own interests as it broadcasts audible messages to me as well as to its own species. All this little citizen of the world requires is fluency in an easy language and the respect of our paying attention and listening.

Compare this to human society and its reactions to COVID-19. The novel coronavirus has in many ways been experienced as a loss-of-connection disease, beginning with those governments who have lost touch with their people when they prioritize economic exchange to the detriment of saving lives. Besides the mortality rate and myriad debilitating symptoms of long COVID, there are mental health challenges from social isolation. Distance work and learning is exasperating preexisting conditions of stress and overwork for adults, let alone children. Western society attempts to carry on as normal through technology and without the relief of either enough alone time or being in the presence of others outside the household. The healthier approach would be to slow down and listen to the warnings of health officials and the long COVID community (surely, they are our sentinel chipmunks). Rather than feeling a loss of typical modern connectivity (itself an exacerbation of a preexisting disease of disconnection to self), perhaps we can understand Pandemic '20–21 as an opportunity to *gain* in connectivity to nature and therefore to healing.

For myself, peace has come with recognizing and addressing things that have kept me from feeling calm and therefore healthy even before the pandemic. COVID-19 is a virus. It didn't attack me because I had been overworking previously. Becoming ill, however, required me to delve into anything weighing on me. As I mentioned in Chapter 5, I am not strong enough to carry around extra burdens after a severe attack to multiple organs. CV-19 may have initially plunged me into a dark night of the soul, but it is now giving me an opportunity to confront the demons that attempt to derail my inner peace.

COVID has been so bewildering a disease because it causes many different symptoms and, for long haulers, uncertain prognoses. As I learn more about healing my own psyche and its related effect on physical health, I can't help but think of the novel coronavirus as a very personal disease. Certain preexisting conditions make adults of any age particularly vulnerable (e.g., cancer, type 2 diabetes mellitus, heart conditions, obesity, asthma, dementia, and hypertension or high blood pressure). Some of these items are caused by larger social forces. Over time, stress can lead to a higher risk of diabetes, asthma, heart disease, gastrointestinal problems, Alzheimer's, obesity and hypertension. That's alarming, even if you are not thinking about COVID-19. Chipmunks can scurry around with high energy, constantly vigilant for predators. They probably have a way of managing this constant fight or flight response, but this continual adrenaline rush is unhealthy among humans. Already in the months before contracting CV-19, I had begun to feel depressed because of stress and overwork.

What *are* our community values, and how do they affect individual and global wellness? As early as August, I reflected on how the long-term healing process was essentially forcing me to recalibrate my approach to life. For years, the stresses in my life were increasing exponentially through the fast pace of overwork and it wasn't going to end well. Abigail had a term for it: "nervous system tense," which means that the nervous system is pressing too hard. This physical reaction occurs when trying to fight off infection, and when being ambitious and driven. If it continues too long, the nervous system weakens. Luckily, I hadn't yet gotten to that point; there's time to reverse what I was doing to myself. This is what I meant when I introduced this book with the proposition that there are some positives to having contracted a long-haul illness. It forces you to learn how to inhabit your body differently, as a friend with Lyme disease put it.

The fatigue of COVID-19 is a viral reaction, but it also seems strangely appropriate in our stressful modern lives because it requires a forced stop or slowing, rather than a pushing forward to do more. In my case, I learned in August to say to my body when suffering a return of nausea and other symptoms, "Well done. Thank you for fighting the disease. You can stop going into overdrive now. I'm okay." Rather than letting intense fear of my prognosis initiate malaise, I focused on settling down the nervous system and my anxiety. It helped to have a health care provider who assessed what was happening and offered hope: "You do not need to be afraid. There is no alarm here." At night, I fell asleep reassuring myself. In the face of fear, I told myself that it was okay.

CRWD

November 1 – All Souls Day. We had a family party last night in lieu of trick-or-treating. Infections are on the rise and my parents' flamboyantly decorated neighborhood draws excited little witches and goblins from all over the surrounding region. We did not want to take the risk of coming in contact again with the virus, yet we had to make a good effort since Halloween is one of Hollis's favorite holidays, along with Christmas and his birthday.

During a meal of hotdogs, mulled apple cider and donuts at our cottage, we five played "Guess How Many Candies in the Jar" for a bouncy ball prize. (There were 588.) To a curated mix of kids' Halloween music, we competed at "Pin the Spider on the Spiderweb," ate sweets and watched Hollis carry out a candy hunt. He found all but two pieces of Bazooka Bubblegum and two mini chocolate bars. They remain hidden since we adults can't recall where we put them.

By the end of the evening, "My mouth hurts," Hollis volunteered. "I've been smiling so much."

Success!

The next morning, orange-brown leaves stick out of little white mounds of pristine snow, as if earth had donned a mottled leopard skin to join the costumed festivities late on Halloween. The holiday spread out over the following days as our son frequently reminded me of Chipmunk storing food for later. In Hollis's case, however, he has a stash of candy that he claims will last him until Easter. He puts it in his coat pocket (instead of his cheeks) and doles it out during long walks with his grandmother. She's happy to walk and he delights in excuses for sweeties, so they enjoy their time together in their own ways. (The candy lasted for only one week.)

With the clocks set back an hour today with the end of daylight saving time, the cats and I have enjoyed being warm in bed, snow falling, wind gusting and leaves occasionally fluttering off their branches, a process to which our grey kitty gives her full attention. She sits at the end of the bed, centered in the window, watching round-eyed.

The atmosphere is a bit like "Winter Time," the poem by Robert Louis Stevenson who was himself often bedridden with illness beginning in childhood:

LATE lies the wintry sun a-bed,
A frosty, fiery sleepy-head;
...

The cold wind burns my face, and blows
Its frosty pepper up my nose.

Black are my steps on silver sod;
Thick blows my frosty breath abroad;
And tree and house, and hill and lake,
Are frosted like a wedding-cake. (1–2, 15–20)

The white blanketing the world outside suggests Stevenson's poem as we lie late in bed like the white wintery sun. The *yin-yang* adjectives "frosty, fiery" suggests a further correlation between the poet's frequent fevers and COVID-19. The latter is like the tropical diseases of malaria and dengue fever in that it waxes and wanes. My particular complaint – the liver – is linked to surplus heat. Metaphorically, traditional Chinese medicine refers to splitting open the pericardium to bathe the open chest in cold snow. With the coming of winter, I have noticed that I have better energy and health on cold days. Being in the cool cottage has also been much easier for me than for other family members, who feel the cold more when they visit. In a very real sense, my relief originates with bathing the *shen* of the whole person in the coolness of new snow.

The quiet in "Winter Time" is apropos to my surroundings, too. Despite Stevenson's love of music, experimentation with song structures in his late poems and the fact that "Winter Time" first appeared in 1885 in a volume titled *Penny Whistles* (a book now known as *A Child's Garden of Verses*), the poem cocoons itself in silence. Active images and chilly feelings persist from the first to the last of the five stanzas, but even the cold wind blows inaudibly. The only sound is in the verse itself: the soft sibilant "s" repeating like the snow in the landscape.

Sonic elements occur through rhythm and pace, too. In this case, a regular iambic tetrameter (a pattern of four slack/stresses) trips along as do nursery rhymes. Occasional variations in this meter serve to pause the poem, as in the final quatrain cited above. This last stanza begins with a stressed word ("Black"), which slows the pace and emphasizes the contrast in color of the footsteps on the silvery ground. The following line's double stress ("Thick blows") lengthens these words like frosty breath lingering in the air. The reader stills with the child's sense of awe, a wonder then rendered in wedding-cake imagery along with an increase of pace in the final couplet.

Now in Michigan, the wild life is quiet if the wind is not. Even yesterday, we still heard Chipmunk's intermittent chipping as she stood guard on the porch railing or ran trilling away from my footfall. Today, Chipmunk is neither seen nor heard, her scurry replaced by Eurus the East Wind catching the fluttering hammock harnesses (still tethered to the trees), waving pine needles and camel-colored leaves, and sending the falling snow into a slanted descent.

Although Bear's dormancy is a month away in this part of Michigan, Chipmunk will begin to hibernate at a deeper level in about three weeks. In their true hibernation, with a regular waking to move about and raise their temperature, chipmunks model an uneven oscillation between unconscious slumber and fits of activity.

Winter motion is like that, too. There is always a leap of joy at first snow – a sudden recognition of something special happening. The flurry of storms cause our female cat to observe more closely than she has all autumn, suggesting the novelty of changing natural rhythms. Children, too, hold their breath as they watch the falling snow from the window: a brief pause of quiet wonder before racing for coat, boots and mittens. Then they dance with delight, tongues outstretched to taste the flakes from above in a first snow celebration.

෴

Gold light through morning trees, creaking in the wind. My new joke is that I've become fluent in chipmunk. Seriously, though, my entire experience of the woods has shifted. What I had perceived as a quiet environment enlivened atmospherically by pretty sounds is now a little overwhelming. I hear frequent warnings, which have me peering all around to spot the threat. It's exhausting at first, but soon settles down into simple literacy.

With this fresh awareness that the animals are not only communicating, but also that we can know what they're saying, I decide to attempt to become a true citizen of the forest by learning to identify birdsongs, too. It is slightly easier to do it now in the relative quiet of the cold season. In contrast, the loud summer teems with wildlife that can be heard, if not always seen. It will take me awhile because birds such as my favorite black-capped chickadees communicate with great complexity. Just like Chipmunk, avian sounds alert us to what others perceive about the world and how they interact with it. It seems amazing to me now that I have treated them like atmospheric muzak, rather than as beings in (and with) their own rights.

11 | Bald Eagle

THE day before the 2020 US presidential election, my sneakers crunch through leaves in the conservancy still brittle from last night's snow. Every now and then as I make my way north along the lakeshore, the wind bends the trees so extremely that a loud crack ricochets through the air. Ahead, I glimpse feathered blue. With my camera ready, I creep slowly, carefully, but the jay disappears by the time that I reach the branch where he had alighted.

The call of seagulls draws me to the water's edge. A flock (a "colony") wheel and circle, climbing and diving until they settle on the choppy water. Aside from their caws and the cracking trees, the forest is quiet on this early winter afternoon. How different from summer, when the woods are alive with birdsong, companion calls and predator alerts from several plumed species, including the laughing whoop of the loon and the sharp drumming of pileated and red-bellied woodpeckers. The honking of Canada geese further enlivens the lakes with the sonority of migration in autumn. With first snow, however, a curtain of avian silence descends.

The air awakens instead with wildly swaying trees, bending from halfway down their trunks. This genuflecting dance is clearly visible through branches bare except for a few tenacious dull gold and burnt-orange leaves. The wind rushes through the forest, unchecked by foliage that instead fully carpets the moss, the two-track, the bluff-side stairs and the muddy path from which I have stepped. On the lake, the wind kicks up ripples in competing directions and bends the tasseled long grasses together, whispering on the shore like the humming chorus in Puccini's *Madama Butterfly*, "Coro a bocca chiusa."

And then overhead in the windy quiet, I see the dark wing span and the flash of white on its head. Bald Eagle! Circling over the water, gaining altitude and flying with silent speed from the east toward the tree-lined southwestern stretch of the land conservancy, it is so swift that its crown shines only for a moment in the sun before it is too high to see. The eagle's velocity makes me realize one reason why sightings are rare. I snap a picture just before it disappears from view, flying upward over the deeply forested wild.

Later, the enlarged image on my laptop verifies that I had indeed seen an eagle. With its white head and mottled brown tail, it seemed to be a juvenile. There it was, visual evidence of a rare sighting: an eagle winging its way up and disappearing. According to the Ojibwe, it was *en route* to the Creator. The first people of Michigan consider bald eagles to be sacred messengers to the heavens, carrying prayers and bringing healing. As this bald eagle flies over wild land the day before the US election, I hope that it is a good omen for personal and national healing, and for peace at the polls. It seems suitable to unite these ideas in my own prayer. Indian confederacies of peace inspired the idea of representative democracy, beginning with the Iroquois Great League of Peace in 1142. More locally, the Council of Three Fires – comprising the Odawa, Ojibwe and Bodéwadmi nations – brought together a peaceful trading alliance among the indigenous lake people.

For myself, I had thought that a bald eagle might be near to the cottage because of Chipmunk's warning. However, because it did not then show itself to me, the previous chapter focused on Chipmunk's lessons. Yet I continued to hope that the unseen raptor would reveal itself. Now, while I focused on two other feathered species (the elusive jay and the prevalent gull), it has.

On a symbolic level, the eagle was unlike the other vertebrates thus far encountered: I hoped to see it and it showed itself. It leads me to ask, "What is faith?"

I believe that courage and faith together contribute to healing. Sometimes people begin to pray (those who have never prayed before) when they feel powerless to direct an outcome in their lives. Feeling helpless motivates them to seek guidance, strength or healing. Yet E.M. Forster's character, Mr. Eager in *A Room With a View*, offers a reminder about a different sort of prayer. In this novel published in 1908, Lucy Honeychurch screams when her party is caught in a tremendous storm after dark. "Courage, Miss Honeychurch, courage and faith," says Eager. He then explains that there's blasphemy in horror, for it suggests that we think that the storm has been called for the express purpose of extinguishing us. "Courage—courage and faith," he repeats (108). Courage, by being linked conjunctively to faith ("and") indicates that the two qualities go together; it is not a causal relationship.

In nineteenth-century Britain, faith was at the heart of intense, ongoing debate. The Enlightenment of the previous century emphasized empiricism (knowledge that comes from sensory observation) simultaneous with a corresponding growth in industry, laissez-faire economics and urban centers. A keyword of the 1800s was therefore progress. As a result of the rapid pace of modernization, Victorians worried that something in the human spirit was getting lost. How could religious belief coexist with material culture?

Our great literary heritage includes reflections about a world that seems to lack metaphysical structure in large part because of the then-new Darwinian narrative of life as a combative struggle and a survival of the fittest based not on worth, but rather more randomly on the environment in which an individual happened to exist. Thus a blue creature stands less chance of surviving in a yellow habitat than does a yellow creature.

Matthew Arnold's poem, "Dover Beach" (1867), is one of the most famous considerations of the loss of faith:

> The Sea of Faith
> Was once, too, at the full, and round earth's shore
> Lay like the folds of a bright girdle furl'd.
> But now I only hear
> Its melancholy, long, withdrawing roar,
> Retreating, to the breath
> Of the night-wind, down the vast edges drear
> And naked shingles of the world. (21–8)

"Dover Beach" expresses how civilization used to have a "full" "Sea of Faith," but this sea is now "withdrawing" like the tide. When we are asked to "Listen!" (9), it is to the grating roughness of waves and the flinging of pebbles, or the emotional state of a world that is contrasted to Faith. The latter seems less real and more like an elaborate figure of speech, as the speaker conveys it: "folds of a bright girdle furl'd."

As with the tide, faith will return through loving human relationships that face the reality of a world in pain:

> Ah, love, let us be true
> To one another! for the world, which seems
> To lie before us like a land of dreams,
> So various, so beautiful, so new,
> Hath really neither joy, nor love, nor light,
> Nor certitude, nor peace, nor help for pain; (29–34)

Having faith, or believing in something beyond the "confused alarms of struggle and flight, / Where ignorant armies clash by night" (36–7), occurs through the heart itself.

There is symbolic truth, too, in Ojibwe ceremonies to cure illness. This culture believes that healing will occur as the eagle wings its way to the Creator, so long as the person casting up the prayer believes in it. Believing helps healing to happen. This perspective is frequently discounted in Western culture, as if prayer or acupuncture is a placebo. However, the symbolism of Eagle suggests another perspective.

We can probably agree that if we want to be ready to seize opportunities when they present themselves, then we need to ready the soil with our efforts. The heart must similarly be ready to receive. Prayer requests aid beyond what we can understand and signals a receptivity to what is offered. It seems to me that the desire to reach a state of faith and acceptance is close to the calm state of mind/body health promoted in traditional Chinese medicine, for prayer also encapsulates the ideas represented in the two pictograms representing the *shen* of the heart and the whole person. The first character indicates the spiritual in the sense of the presence of ancestors. The second signifies reaching out to connect. To practice faith (in the metaphysical sense and in the need for connectivity) is at the root of what it means to be a healthy person.

Faith also motivates. In the previous chapter, I knew that if I was meant to see the bird to which Chipmunk alerted me, then I would. I remembered neighbors' sightings of the eagle and articulated a desire to see this avian presence for myself. I prepared and was even lucky enough to have my camera ready when Eagle finally appeared. I stood gazing up to the heavens in order first to see it and then to watch its soaring flight. Surely this looking up is as much a stance of prayer as is the humbly bowed head.

Eagle's flight represents the message to the gods, embodied. In Anishinaabek belief, the medicine man or woman might imagine him or herself as the eagle who takes the prayer of healing, or the illness itself, up to the Creator (French). The emissary is thus the message and the sickness itself; or, prayer and healing together. Understanding oneself to become Eagle embodying both illness and healing prayer requires one to have faith in something beyond oneself and, simultaneously, to tap into an intrinsic personal power. This orientation leads to the perception of oneness, by which we heal ourselves in a deliberate intent to engage with the natural and spiritual world. It posits a mutuality: I am the Eagle; the Eagle is me.

The Odawa view the eagle as a warrior, moreover. Prayer is therefore active, courageous and loving. Love in this sense knows how to protect the heart. The pericardium – the membrane around the heart – physically shields the heart from infection and malignancy; emotionally it can be imagined as both letting people in and barring entry when it senses a threat. Abigail mentioned to me in one of our acupuncture treatments that if we think of the body like an emperor's court, then the pericardium is the emperor's lap dog: a chow who wags its tail in welcome for friends, but who barks at the approach of an enemy. Functioning as a discerning gate-keeper, the guard dog protects the heart against those who would attach themselves to a person for their own needs.

This lesson came about when I suddenly developed an itchy, spreading rash. Many long haulers experience rashes. I did not know this at the time. Because my rash began in areas that were pericardium points, I addressed it for the most part by engaging in an emotional housecleaning whereby I reclaimed my own soul by recognizing when my inner chow had been attempting to warn me about some selfish people whom I had let close to my heart. It was important to reconstruct my encounters with them as experiences, rather than having to do with my *shen* (of the heart; of the spirit). As I worked through this process, the rash eventually disappeared.

Because this was an uncomfortable experience, I made use of some herbal treatments, too. Later, back in St. Louis, I learned that histamines are released by heat and that many long haulers found a cold rinse at the end of a shower to be helpful in reducing itchiness. That made me laugh. I had sometimes endured tepid showers at Polly's house, where the hot water heater had been turned down low for the off season. They were the least favorite part of my dry cabin experience, but occasionally it wasn't possible to shower at Mom and Dad's. Sometimes there was bad weather or intense fatigue that kept me from making the trek to their house. Then, I braved the lukewarm water and, simultaneously, provided a cooling salve.

The eagle spirit offers a different sort of aid in comparison to the guardian chow. Unlike the protectiveness of the pericardium, we can intentionally open ourselves to divine relationships. In indigenous American cultures, the Creator's intervention requires the gift of a sacred plant. "Tobacco offerings in the fire," Edward Benton-Banai writes in the story of "The Pipe and the Eagle," were understood as a means to carry "thoughts and prayers to the Creator" through the medium of smoke (80). Offertory tobacco aligns with the actions of "humble people" who try "to live in harmony with the Universe" (80) and thus communicates the state of being with which the supplicant approaches prayer. In offering tobacco, the Anishinaabek actively recognize a participatory and mutual relationship with creation, showing respect, thanksgiving and humility. This gift of tobacco is an act of prayer itself.

Thinking about how to communicate spiritual reverence and thanksgiving, I find myself moved to enact an exchange with the universe. I do not feel the deep spiritual meaning of tobacco since my culture is different from indigenous America, and appropriation seems disrespectful. What makes sense to me is more of an attitude where I take a moment at the start of each day to pause in appreciation of the natural world and to say thank you. I try to give back when situations present themselves, too, from putting up birdfeeders (when bears are absent), reducing my footprint on the planet (conserving, composting, recycling, reusing), giving charitably to a tree-planting foundation, and making a family commitment to planting trees. What feels most important to me, however, is that daily renewal of an intent to give with gratitude. This calibration will, I think, help to maintain the health of personhood in relation to the larger universe even when I return to work.

The desire to become more thoughtful to the earth brings something divine with it. As we express our thanksgiving to animate nature, that intentional act also opens ourselves to recognize and receive grace. The universe's regenerating spirit is freely given, but sometimes we do not recognize it when it occurs. I now view COVID-19 and this medical leave as acts of grace because my holistic life is improving. This perspective required me to go on a healing journey in order to discard workaholic values and behaviors, to shed the non-self and to quest, instead, for what makes a whole person.

This writing itself embodies a prayer for holistic healing and a shift of direction, too. It was, in fact, the most important therapy that I undertook. Through journaling, I came to insights that would have been impossible without writing down my thoughts; the process balances intuition with intellect. Now, I am offering a prayer for the larger community through sharing it in published form and dedicating it to you, the reader.

The desire to help oneself, to be helped and to help others is symbolized by the eagle who acts on behalf of human survival. In Christianity, Jesus carries the grace of God in much the same way. In Benton-Banai's story, "The Pipe and the Eagle," the winged messenger intervened just before sunrise to plead with the Creator for the earth's survival because, while human beings had begun to operate in harmful ways to each other, there yet existed people who lived honorable, prayerful lives. The Eagle also made his case for the sake of a future which might yet correct the selfishness of those few who used power for personal gain. A deal was made in the legend: Eagle would report daily to the Creator on the state of humanity and the sun would rise again. Of this story of rebirth and second chances, Benton-Banai concludes: "We owe our lives and the lives of our children to the eagle ... remember our brother, the eagle, and the role he plays in the preservation of the Earth" (82). The eagle, the head of the Bird Clan, was like his totem family in his intuitive and prophetic knowledge (76).

The eagle, with a mind as elevated as his flight according to Benton-Banai, perceives both the act of good faith and the potential for a future where individuals act with integrity. The Creator is influenced by the intentions of the people to be prayerful, honest and humble. This goal for tomorrow, the eagle's intervention and the Creator's grace triangulate to save humanity. What the eagle has preserved humanity for is a better awareness of a humble and grateful relationship with the universe.

This Anishinaabek spirit truth is passed down through the generations by a story, but it is also intimately learned as a patient. As I heal from long COVID, I find myself naturally interacting with lessons given elsewhere in Benton-Banai's stories: "To honor all of the Creation is to have RESPECT" and "HUMILITY is to know yourself as a sacred part of the Creation" (64). This dignified orientation is also how I, as a patient, wish to be treated by the medical establishment.

ᏟᎬᏇᎠ

It is Friday of election week (November 6, 2020) and we're still waiting for all the votes to be counted. The pandemic spreads ever more rapidly, reaching 100,000 new infections daily this week in the USA. As the sun rises today, the third day since the election (and the fourth since I saw the bald eagle flying), it seems relevant that Eagle can be understood not only as a healing messenger, but also as a supplicant on behalf of a world that has the potential (and the need) to become better. We must try to address and recover from the violence of racism, misogyny, shaming and bullying that have been devastating to our society on top of (and entangled with) the sufferings caused by the pandemic.

While we await the outcome of the election, I am reminded of how the United States originally intended to represent itself. The Secretary of the Continental Congress, Charles Thompson, designed a seal for the fledging nation showing a bald eagle, wings outspread, clutching the symbols of war and peace in its talons – an olive branch and thirteen arrows (the same number as the original colonies). Within a shield on the eagle's breast, the red and white chevrons above a blue field symbolized valor, purity, vigilance, perseverance and justice, writes US National Archives blogger, Meagan T. Frenzer.

The eagle is in flight between earth (a horizontal line under the eagle on the original shield) and the light of the heavens above (rays above the clouds that extend downward to bathe the eagle and the land in divine light). Surely this is the eagle messenger between the land and the heavens, a radiantly spiritual being, overseeing justice not only among humans (the courts of law), but also requesting divine blessing. It is a symbol of valor in the best sense: in service of a vigilant upholding of purity. This is what our nation needs to heal division and hate. It is what valiant individuals who persevere in their struggle for health require. At root, I wonder if we can see similarities with the Ojibwe story of "The Pipe and the Eagle."

It reminds me, too, of another inaugural moment, when Maya Angelou wrote "On the Pulse of Morning" for Bill Clinton's first presidency in 1993.

Here, on the pulse of this fine day
You may have the courage
To look up and out and upon me,
The Rock, the River, the Tree, your country.
...

And say simply
Very simply
With hope—
Good morning. (100–3, 111–4)

These terminal lines of the poem herald a beginning – our national rebirth – through greeting the world with the reminder that we *are* the rock, the river and the tree. Observing the land with which we identify inspires hope and faith.

C3&O

On the fourth day, the election has been called. How moving that Joe Biden drew his victory speech to conclusion by offering a hymn: "He will raise you up on eagle's wings," by Roman Catholic priest Jan Michael Joncas. Biden revealed that he'd been thinking about this sound of solace in the last days of the campaign: "It captures the faith that sustains me and which I believe sustains America." He read aloud these words from the hymn, based on Psalm 91:

And He will raise you up on eagle's wings,
Bear you on the breath of dawn,
Make you to shine like the sun,
And hold you in the palm of His hand.

Biden hoped that the words would comfort all of those over "230,000 families who have lost a loved one to this terrible virus this year." To me, the hymn also offers solace to those of us healing, both from the virus and the way that Americans have treated each other for holding different political views.

Biden concluded with a broader sense of the need to regain health: "And now, together – on eagle's wings – we embark on the work that God and history have called upon us to do ... with faith in America and in each other." Let us be, he said, "A nation healed." He finished by calling upon God's blessings for our country and our troops, who are surely like our eagle warriors.

HILE I was driving home in the depth of winter, a crow black as midnight flew down the road to meet me. I've never before seen a bird follow the path of a road, as if it marked both a terrestrial and an aerial route. More often, four-footed and feathered creatures cross roads; they scurry or swoop to avoid an approaching vehicle, quickly hiding again in the undergrowth or canopy. This crow, however, flew straight toward me at the height of a two-story building. Maybe it kept flying along the road at the same altitude after we met, but I like to imagine that it angled slightly up, as if flying to the heavens.

The Leech Lake Band of Ojibwe in Minnesota have passed down a story that seems relevant to the appearance of Crow at this point in my life. In "A Story About Crow: Andek," the black-feathered bird is distressed to find that he has no purpose in life. Andek travels to each of his fellow creatures to learn what role the Great Spirit has given to them. Eventually, he comes across animals in pain. Sometimes he directs them to other species whose purpose is to help, such as Bear who is a healer. Alternatively, Crow observes the hurt creature's unique characteristics and suggests remedies. In this way, he discovers that his purpose is to assist or guide others. "A Story About Crow" concludes, "Andek is our traveling companion always rem—"

In the middle of writing "reminding," I looked up to see two deer calmly looking in my bedroom window at me, about twenty feet away. They were young, supple and gentle in their gaze. The color of the fallen leaves, they were perfectly camouflaged and therefore at one with the environment. As I got up, we walked in parallel – me to the living room and they toward the conservancy – pacing together, watching. Given their bearing, it seems entirely right that the Anishinaabek commemorate a warrior's dream of "a deer who danced in the heavens." The Indian dance is meant to enact the deer's character: "grace, watchfulness, and gentility." To Basil Johnston, a dance's "countless beats and various rhythms" embody what he so aptly calls "the mood of the soul" (147, 146).

As I looked from the living room, I saw new deer; there were twice as many as I had first seen framed by the bedroom window. Four deer looked in on me with peace in their eyes. Hinds and fawns stood *deux par deux*, first one pair holding my gaze before bounding off, white tails highlighted against fawn-colored leaves. They raced off not in fear, but rather because they were already *en route*. Their pause in wonder at the sight of me was a mirror of my awe at seeing them. The original pair then stepped up to the living room window, holding my gaze with strength and power, before they, too, leapt away, first one then the other.

What makes these encounters of crow and deer significant is their particular interactions with me. I've been seeing and hearing the female deer and their offspring all summer, only I thought it was a trio (a doe and two fawns). The doe would stand in the road looking at me, waiting until I ventured too close before springing away. Or Hollis and I would hear their many-hooved crash through the undergrowth and glimpse their leaping progress through the conservancy or around the colony cottages. What happened this morning, however, was prolonged curiosity on the herd's part, peering through the windows and holding my gaze while we paced in tandem.

Deer eyes are particularly sensitive. They see extremely well at night because their eyes contain more rods than cones. These gentle animals freeze in the headlights of moving vehicles because it takes longer for their eyes to adjust to the sudden brightness. Standing as close as I did this morning, the power of their liquid orbs felt like falling into a universe of supple-strong peace. The calm eloquence had a potency, unlike the gaze that I had locked with Chipmunk, when I could not parse the urgent warning. Here, the deer eyes opened up new conceptions, soundlessly. Both the method and the meaning was beyond language. They were the deep soul of the world.

When the hibernators of the animal world have wrapped themselves in sleep under the snow, the deer, crows and squirrels remain active. The latter two are ubiquitous, unlike the seldom-seen deer. The black squirrel population outnumbers the grey squirrels in this part of the world, so the wildlife mostly shines black-feathered and black-furred against sparkling snow, charcoal-grey tree trunks and watery sky.

It seems relevant to me that the guide animal, Crow, would appear in a singular fashion right now, for I've been wondering as I cross the halfway mark of my medical leave how I am going to manage reentry to my professional life. I'm confident now that I will work again. A couple of weeks ago I was beginning to take fifteen- or twenty-minute walks every few days to the arrow tree and back, resulting in fatigue but not nausea. Now, I am tired, but more in the manner of exertion and being out of shape, rather than tipping over into outright illness.

This week, I've had a leap forward in my health. I am now able to walk thirty to forty minutes without setback. I pass the arrow tree in both directions now and always affectionately acknowledge it as a tree marking my way. To the Little Traverse Bay Bands of Ottawa Indians, Eric Hemenway tells us that bent trees "were ways to signal where you were or if there was lodging up ahead. These trees told that. They had messages" (Driscoll). As I make my return journey, there is indeed hospitality ahead for me. While Hemenway intended trail navigation, I find that his words resonate with my continual approach to the tree in search of how it might inspire me to map my life. Soon, I will be thinking not only of walking this Interlochen path, but also how to maintain my equilibrium as my radius increases in the return to St. Louis.

This same week, the announcement of a vaccine from Pfizer with over 90% efficacy makes it seem as if some wealthy countries might have a return to face-to-face life rather sooner than health experts and scientists had originally believed to be possible. There are many questions yet to be answered, including how distribution will work to all nations, but this is nevertheless solid progress. I find that I suddenly want to make plans again: What would I like to do when this is over? Where shall we go?

Such thoughts necessarily return me to wondering about the practicalities of my return to work. I'm fortunate to have a job that I love, but how can I be the new version of me and not resume the high level of stress that had become my norm? I don't know exactly how to accomplish a healthy balance during working life.

Perhaps Crow can provide some guidance if we return to the story told by the Leech Lake Band of Ojibwe. Here is the full quotation from the story of Andek that was interrupted mid-word when two deer peered in my window:

> Andek is our traveling companion[,] always reminding us that work and dedication will show the way to the purpose we seek. We cannot find our purpose if we sit on the path. Crow teaches that you must meet life head-on and create good connections with those around you and work with [the] spirit of friendship.
>
> As Andek found out, you become your purpose by doing what feels good with good intention. Walk a good path and you will be guarantee[d] to find your life's purpose.

Funny how Crow met me "head-on" as I drove. This is perhaps the answer: to continue following my vocational calling, but with the intention to continue the mindfulness of now. This way of being interacts with the world in mutually respectful ways, including with the people in my life (the lesson of the doe). It sounds so simple, but it is nevertheless as profound as the peace in hart eyes. For the quartet of gentle deer communicated serenity even during the fearful adrenalin rush of hunting season.

The path forward is like the road that I traveled when Crow appeared. All three of my childhood homes sit on this road, but State Park Highway is paved in its northern segment. The little dirt turning leading to our cottage is across from a yellow diamond road sign, "PAVEMENT ENDS." Three hundred yards later, the asphalt becomes a dirt road, pitted with potholes and rutted from infrequent traffic. Instead of houses set close to each other, the dozen driveways along this mile-long southern segment mostly disappear into dense forest. Eventually, the so-called "highway" tees off at a paved road which, if you turn left, continues its course through wild countryside for two more miles before transitioning to farmland.

What is unusual about this unpaved section of road is that I travel it daily now as the shortest route to my parents. When I was growing up, however, we rarely travelled past the pavement's end. Crow thus met me as I drove back to the cottage on a path that was unfrequented in childhood. It is both part of home and a new way, like the intuitive guidance that I am learning to live by: part of me, but previously underutilized in favor of critical-rational thinking.

Crow, nesting high in the trees, symbolizes insight as it makes its home near the heavens. Like the Leech Lake Band of Ojibwe story, what Andek knows will help those who follow his guidance. Strangely, as I began to decipher Crow's meaning, highly social creatures stepped up to my window to gaze in, be present with me and exemplify how to be gentle, aware participants in group life, bringing grace to others. Mid-sentence, a duet of deer looked in on me, offering insight because I looked back with openness and wonder.

Thinking about paths of life recalls the *Tao Te Ching* ("The Way of Life"). Chapter LII contains an editorial note explaining that the passage below refers to the senses ("openings") and the intellect:

> Block the openings,
> Shut the doors,
> And all your life you will not run dry.
> Unblock the openings,
> Add to your troubles,
> And to the end of your days you will be beyond salvation. (LII, 118)

Taoists would love that intuition flew at me as I travelled the unpaved path of life and then again, looked in at me as I wrote about Crow in my journal. The above lines have to do with intuition, too, rather than empirical or critical-rational knowing. "The way to do is to be," as the terminal line in Chapter XLVII so memorably puts it. Trying to do otherwise, as I worried about reentry to working life and tried to *make sense* of it, was only troubling me. Metaphorically speaking, rather than trying to peer through the windows of the future, I looked up and saw the deer gently gazing in.

Another version of Chapter XLVII of Lao Tzu's treatise probably best embodies the spirit of Taoism. Here is Witter Bynner's translation:

> There is no need to run outside
> For better seeing,
> Nor to peer from a window. Rather, abide
> At the center of your being;
> For the more you leave it, the less you learn.
> Search your heart and see

A rather nice pun on this morning's experience might be "Search the *hart* and see." Sight in this instance refers to physical and inner sight, the latter found by looking in the doe's eyes – a locked exchange of (a) vision.

If I search my *heart* and see, I find that luminous peace expressed in the deer eyes and I understand my path to hold fast to this way of being. The "doing" will happen naturally. My current path is a good one. Emerging from my liminal experience includes reflecting on how to make the transition. Liminal, an anthropological concept from Arnold van Gennep's *Rites de Passage* (1909), refers to a playful time and place apart from normal social life, where an initiate experiences transition from one life state to another. Essentially, this line of thinking highlights the socialized sense of self, where one exists in relation to external expectations, including workloads. How can I continue to experience a more holistic sense of self amidst the heavy requirements of a university job? The answer deepens the lesson of Chapter 1, which considered post-Enlightenment Western identity as including second-order observation (being evaluated by another as in therapy or the internalized process of self-evaluation, such as judging self-worth by workaholic productivity).

There are other social models, however, as represented by lake and river networks. "Highest good is like water," begins Chapter VIII of the *Tao Te Ching*. "Because water excels in benefiting the myriad creatures without contending with them and settles where none would like to be, it comes close to the way" (20). Reading my annotations of Tzu's poem, I once again return to my beginnings to make sense of my present and my future. My sixteen-year-old self learned these lessons just two miles away from my present location:

Water-like behavior:
    flows
    moves without effort
    seeks the lowest point – humility
    adaptable – fits into any area or surrounding
    goes into earth to help plant growth – constant cycle
    strength – yet not imposing strength – erosion

Yes: much of this text and my marginalia still resonates with me today. Growing up near coastal Michigan or its river valleys tends to form a water-oriented child. In the previous chapter, I ruminated on humility (point 3 above). Now, the idea of adaptability (number 4) offers reassurance as I contemplate reentry. The final aspect of non-imposing strength seems relevant, too, in a chapter about the graceful deer. I remember the discussion surrounding that last point, led by our teacher, Mr. Hintze. Water does not seem to be strong and yet erosion gradually occurs with the gentle, repetitive motion of the river.

As the terminal line of Chapter VIII clarifies, a peaceful approach to life is a way that excels: "It is because it does not contend that it is never at fault" (22).

At fault with who?

Previously, I had thought that this line referred to one's relationships within a community: some person is at fault. Since the poetic treatise communicates a philosophy about the way of life, however, this non-contending manner is, more expansively, about being in tune with the Tao. Being at one is a life orientation; it is not at "fault" with that way of being.

The "highest good" for everyone, and for one's own well-being, is to discover that liquid calm of doe eyes. Imagine what we could be as a community if more of us found that water-like manner of existence (doing through *flowing* in tune with a peaceful heart). Would that not initiate a world such as Robert Frost imagined in his deer encounter poem? In "Two Look at Two," a human couple see a buck and a doe pass "unscared along the wall" (24):

> Still they stood,
> A great wave from it going over them,
> As if the earth in one unlooked-for favor
> Had made them certain earth returned their love. (39–42)

The poem concludes with a wave of loving reciprocity with the land because of two pairs of fearless, communicative eyes that seem like mother nature's gift. There is a moment of wonder in the encounter – in the pause – before stepping on. How appropriate, moreover, that

Frost published this poem in a Pulitzer Prize-winning book entitled *New Hampshire*, but dedicated to Vermont and Michigan.

In reflecting on the circularity of past and present, it seems relevant that my high school biology teacher and his wife, Steve and Janie Tavener, commented on my anecdote about the deer who came to visit me: "Perhaps they were trying to communicate with you," they wrote on Facebook. It certainly seemed that way to me. Why shouldn't wild animals seek to communicate with us? And why shouldn't we learn from them?

When I was fourteen, this same teacher took a group of us camping on Beaver Island. Lake Michigan's largest island is part of the archipelago homelands for Waganakising Odawak living in northwestern lower Michigan. Mr. Tavener showed us how to catch fish with our bare hands. You ease your hand into a river, hold it still by the side of the bank, wait for a fish to swim by and then pick it up. I have a photo of my success just before I carefully let it wriggle back to the water and its freedom. When we are calm and at one with nature, intending no harm, it swims right up to you.

What I am learning from the deer is not only a stillness in being that has peace at its center, but also that it is through being at peace that I can best approach decisions and even difficult moments. This state brings holistic well-being, and seems to resonate on a frequency heard by the natural world to the point that its creatures seek me out as a sister. I find now, as I'm writing, that this is perhaps the highest level of respect to which I can aspire: being at one with the world and being acknowledged as such. There is no need for validation from human accolades. This inner searching of my heart, in a calm center, benefits myriad lifeforms: human, animal and the forest itself. What could be more beautiful?

13 | Black Ice

LACK ice occurs when wet pavement freezes. It is invisible on tarmac and therefore treacherous, being detectable only in the right light or in the slide that results from braking. The conditions were perfect for black ice tonight as I drove back to the cottage at 8:00 p.m. after a windy day of cold rain and falling temperatures. Visibility was now terrible in the pitch dark and snow. Crawling along at forty mph on slippery roads, the snow came straight at me, a blinding flurry in my high beams.

Visibility is better with low beams right now.

Dimming the headlights reminds me of the things that I don't see in the world around me, but that I know are there. My neighbors, Ericka and Andy, continue to hear coyotes in the forest near to their house. Chipmunks still scurry about, and earlier today I saw a bald eagle flying east to west over the Leelanau Peninsula. I've recently learned to marvel when nature reveals herself: to see the miracle in an eagle's flight toward the heavens.

Our black bear is still around, too. Bears in this part of Michigan won't hibernate for two to three weeks yet (at the beginning of December). Candace and Chris, our friends near the swamp, see her muddy pawprints, while Ericka has had another type of encounter.

Thinking that Tootsie Toes must surely be hibernating by early November, she and Andy resumed setting out their bird feeder and suet. The bear began making midnight visits. Ericka saw her once when she got up to investigate a noise. When she switched on the patio light, Tootsie was sitting six feet away with the feeder in one paw. With the other, she was in mid-reach for the suet. Woman and she-bear looked at each other, Makwa five feet tall while seated. The cat froze, too, on her perch inside, unblinking in the ursine presence. Ericka turned off the light. When she returned a few minutes later, Tootsie had lumbered off.

Caution is necessary in a wild place. On windy days like we're having, it can be dangerous to even walk outside in the woods. Normally, we see evidence of a storm in the trees that have fallen across our footpath into the state park. I had to step around two massive fallen trunks last week. Soon, neighbors or park rangers will cut the noble pines into pieces with a chain saw and move the logs aside.

More unusually, I just cleared away part of a fallen tree that lay straight across our dirt road to the south. It was too heavy for me fully to move, but the top had broken off as it fell. I hauled the crown off the road, leaving just enough room to drive past. When I returned later that day, the rest of the tree was lying parallel to the road on the other side. Clearing the path is neighborly.

These fallen trees remind me of the big wheels: the horse-drawn log hauling device preserved by the Interlochen State Park as representative of the area's lumbering history. As children, my brother and I clambered over the logs set up as part of the display and performed gymnastic feats on the spokes of the gigantic red wagon wheels. The world's natural resources seemed inexhaustible in the days of the timber industry a hundred years ago. The lumberjacks' lifestyle is memorialized in 187 acres of old-growth forest here in Interlochen and further north in forty-nine acres at Hartwick Pines, where visitors can see the height and girth of the world as it was. Today, thinking of the logging history makes me sick. It seems ironic that its history is celebrated by those stands of pine that it missed or deliberately set aside, and that the latter was done in awareness that our stunning land would make a desirable holiday destination. The old-growth forest that escaped the axe here in Interlochen was placed under the stewardship of the state in 1917.

Trees fall naturally, of course, and some areas of the woods are laddered with trunk after trunk lying at odd angles on the forest floor. The day after a storm, big chunks of bark continue to tumble off high branches. Sometimes the cause is not what it first seems, as when a pileated woodpecker is responsible. On a recent gusty walk when Hollis was visiting the cottage, he pointed out the red tufted head busily tapping in silence to remove chunks of the soft outer bark, like practice on a drum pad before the loud tattoo to follow. This latter percussive performance declares territorial rights. Either way, the woodpecker procures a dinner of insects and their larvae.

Regardless of the reason why, it is smart to be aware when walking in the woods. I don't carry a cell phone on my walks, but if I did it would be dangerous to walk head down, gazing at my screen and missing the health benefits of forest bathing. My neighbor who does just this may also miss seeing falling bark and branches, thus blinding herself to lessons that literally fall from above.

Today – a blustery day – a long branch broke off about a minute after I passed and fell on the dirt two-track where our cat and I had been meandering. We both froze and stared, before picking up our pace on the way home. It makes me wonder what it is like up in the nests, newly revealed through webs of bare branches that reach toward the heavens like unfurled Spanish fans of black lace. Squirrel nests (dreys) have improbable clusters of leaves, making no sense to my eye. Even wedged into the fork of a tree, how do they hold their shape in high winds? It is an engineering feat of sticks, moss, bark and grass that I cannot see from so far below. Birds' nests, more tightly woven of twigs, mud, grass and feathers, perch even higher in the trees. Eagles make their homes at the top of the tallest trees. I've never seen the aeries, but I know they're there. Eagles return each year to undisturbed habitats, adding new sticks to their home until the aerie reaches about ten feet in diameter.

More visible are the blue jays. Yesterday a male perched high on a spindly branch above me, cocking its head as it looked me in the eye, before fluttering off to join his mate who had flown up from a pine branch down the hill. First one, then the other, alighting on a branch before flitting to a new perch, an aerial leap-frogging. This delightful play helps to draw attention to the need, right now, to observe creaking branches that might fall, unlike the elastic boughs that spring up as avian feet let go in their upward launch.

I'm aware of black ice, too, and the need to lower my headlights in pelting fans of snow because I took driver's education in the Michigan winter. Hours of student driving were clocked on snowy roads with Mr. Tavener, whose inner calm was remarkable during meanders down snow-clad, curling roads lined with pine boughs drooping heavily under their caps of snow. We learned how to stop safely before there were anti-lock brakes, to turn, to come out of a slide, cross snow-encrusted lanes and to be alert to the slippery danger posed by winter slush. Mr. Tavener even turned on the radio, cautioning, "Be careful not to tap your feet to the music." Even seasoned cold-weather drivers have terrible accidents, but not as many because we northern youngsters are warned about hidden dangers and taught how to manage them.

Preventing catastrophe sometimes depends upon drawing knowledge from human history as well as one's own experiences. In the case of not pushing my recovery from COVID-19 and its long aftermath, I was influenced by the example of the 1918–19 Spanish influenza epidemic. Virologist Professor John Oxford reported in May 2020 on a BBC Radio 4 podcast that so many young adults (twenties to forties) died a century ago in "Pandemic 1918" because they pushed themselves. Their elders, however, rested and may also have had some immunity from similar viral outbreaks in the nineteenth century. Listening to this podcast about seven weeks after the onset of our illness enforced my commitment to rest. Friends who had already had the virus counseled the same, as did my doctor and my acupuncturists, first in Missouri and then in Michigan. The body needs all its strength to fight off a major attack and then to build up health again.

It wasn't necessarily easy to stop and rest when needed. There were a few days during November and December when I was unable to make the drive to spend the evening with my family. I could sense their bafflement on the other end of the phone and I felt terrible not being able to see Hollis (and relieve my parents from the childcare). They would query, "What do you think is causing you to feel this way?" It made no sense to me, and being asked made me feel responsible and as if I was disappointing them. They were simply concerned and had no point of comparison, for normally I was able to follow through on the things that we'd planned. Caring for someone with long COVID is extremely difficult on many fronts. Not least, it was upsetting for everyone when we had been looking forward to time together. Sometimes I had not slept well the night before, or I'd had a normal phone conversation that nevertheless left me exhausted. These didn't seem like valid reasons and yet the truth was that my energy was easily sapped and some days could only be spent in bed. I finally began to accept and to respond, simply: "Why? Long COVID."

◯㒷◯

I steer myself through recovery better when I turn off the high beams. It scares me to immerse myself in the media coverage of numerous ongoing problems associated with long COVID. My body seizes up with PTSD and symptoms return, especially a foggy numbness that travels up the back of my head. I then have to work through the anxiety yet again to find the calm state that is proving restorative. It is wise to stay informed and I do, but only by flicking on the high beams momentarily. Then I see that Dr. Mary Fowkes (Head of Autopsy and Neuropathology at Mount Sinai Hospital, New York) found mini-blood clots in the lungs, heart and liver while performing autopsies on people killed by COVID, as well as significant clots in the brain. Clots lead to strokes. When I learned from Anderson Cooper's segment on *60 Minutes* that sixty-six year old Dr. Fowkes had died from an unexpected heart attack on November 15, a week before the episode aired, I quickly turned down the headlights.

While clinics and hospitals in the USA have labelled illness after the live virus phase Post-COVID Syndrome or Post-Acute COVID-19 Syndrome (PACS), this idea of it being "post" seems a misnomer when applied to the lived experience. While I understand that the name signals the post-viral period to doctors or the consequences of a disease (sequelae), the label fails to communicate the patient's sense of continuity in what has happened. PACS is not only the debris after a catastrophe; it *is* the catastrophe. While we expected to be ill from a virus, perhaps violently so, those of us who contracted CV-19 before April were blind-sided by the ongoing and severe impact on health, quality of life and productivity. It is a blessing to have survived the live virus stage, but there's not necessarily a substantive difference between the experiences of COVID and so-called "post" COVID. It's all COVID to me. Those of us who have "PACS" *continue* to try to get well. "Long COVID" – a name coined by Dr. Elisa Perego in a tweet from Lombardy on 20 May 2020 – more adequately expresses the condition from the individual patient's perspective and also from the long-haul community who rapidly grouped together under the twitter hashtag #LongCovid (Callard 737). This nomenclature reflects, too, how the alternative health community understands the disease to deplete energetic reservoirs; it is not "post" because the imprint left by the virus is still there and we are not yet fully recovered.

Not skidding off life's road when long COVID appears out of nowhere reminds me of wilderness survival. Jill Fredston, co-director of the Alaska Mountain Safety Center, offered a memorable lecture to Cambridge Alumni in New York in 2006 that has stuck with me. She concluded by listing the qualities typically held in common among those who survive a disaster in the wilderness. You:

- "Accept the reality," moving quickly through the denial stage, which enables you to deal with the problems;
- "Stay calm" (fear is used to focus, not paralyze);
- "Figure out what the problem is, identify the options," decide on a plan, and break a big task into smaller units;
- Have "a belief that you can succeed" – this is the most important thing, seen in many survival stories;
- "Work to keep your team moving in the same direction and foster a sense of community";
- "Be creative in your use of resources, use humor whenever you can"; and
- Experience "intense appreciation for the beauty of the ocean or the mountain or whatever it was that was about to kill" you, meaning that you are able to see the bigger world and therefore are able to function in it.

Fredston's lecture, "A View from Water Level," addressed conservation and the distressing loss of true wilderness due to human encroachment, but at the time I felt that its applications spread out beyond ecological devastation. We are all having trouble keeping our heads above water. Problems that have strained the entire ecosystem are also making daily life stressful and causing illness in our bodies and communities. The problems are interconnected and they all begin with humanity.

Moreover, Fredston observed, we act surprised when natural disasters occur and are generally very good at springing into action to provide emergency relief aid, rebuild houses and bring back employment. Yet if we pay attention, there are cataclysmic tornadoes, hurricanes, tsunamis and avalanches that strike every month somewhere around the world. They are not that unusual. What Fredston found more striking is human blindness to gradual change, such as global warming, the exhaustion of natural resources and the extinction of animal species as a result of human choices. We are so blind that we effectively accept these more catastrophic problems to animals, environment, and humanity itself.

A virus may not be overtly caused by environmental abuse, but the ways of thinking that have led to a variety of natural disasters are in fact damaging people's attempts to heal as they push themselves to recover physical fitness and to work full days, ignoring fatigue that has similarities to ME/Chronic Fatigue. For years, my stress level has caused alarmed cautions from my nearest family. The level of overwork for a female academic in the top rank had become so extreme as to make me – a naturally upbeat person for whom professional life is a joy – depressed. Statistics show that full professors who are women undertake more administrative work than male colleagues of comparable standing, especially in terms of external service to the profession; social expectations of female gender identity create additional pressure for women to agree when invited to serve (Flaherty; Guarino and Borden). It is a familiar tale along the ivied hallways of the humanities on both sides of the Atlantic. I knew how unhealthy this life-style is, leaving me with few emotional resources. Even before contracting COVID, I had lost my sense of calm center and was probably careening toward stress-induced illness. Yet it's difficult to stop the cycle, both because of the demands and rewards of professional life, and because of habituation. It has taken an extreme illness to break the pattern.

Luckily, I have been in the midst of a mostly supportive community who are advising rest and making it possible for me to do so. Many people worldwide are not in this privileged position and are losing their jobs, not qualifying for insurance or welfare assistance, and needing to manage the stress of disbelief, scoffing, shaming, confrontation and anger on top of feeling extremely unwell, afraid and traumatized. These are familiar and repeated stories in the global long COVID community, as seen in the chat among the tens of thousands of members of support groups on social media. Spouses and life partners are abandoning long haulers, too.

As I attempt to recover my peaceful equilibrium after shining the headlights into the flurry of snowflakes buffeting my windshield (hearing the stories of people struggling with terrifying and sometimes worsening long COVID symptoms), I reexamine Fredston's list. Many other long haulers are showing amazing tenacity and admirable fortitude as they doggedly work to get better. The one element that I have not heard articulated so far is the last bullet point; experiencing long COVID is not usually talked about in terms of appreciation. Certainly, I would have preferred not to become ill, but I can also feel genuine gratitude for how COVID-19 has caused me to slow down so that I don't crash in the speed of modern life; healing from it has helped me to learn to take a different route. On this path, I find thankfulness for wild beauty and for its assistance in healing mind, body and soul.

ψεσ

During the course of my illness, I have sometimes occupied myself by assembling digital family photo books. I had been pushing this daunting task aside for years as the photos piled up. When I was unable to think critically, however, the project suddenly seemed to be a creative engagement with life. It took me months to put together the albums. Now, awaiting the arrival of the printed books feels big, like anticipating the appearance of legacies. These markers of our family life and connections to the past will be stabilizers for Hollis, holding our memories in pictures and anecdotal sayings from before he can himself remember. After we die, they will become visible, material witnesses to people building lives together. Here are the prompts for stories and explanations about our own traces.

I've noticed my Cambridge college similarly adding to its living history. Fellows who were my teachers, friends, lunch companions and colleagues gradually appear as names on buildings or in oil paintings on the walls. The people of the past grace the titles of scholarships and fellowships. Plaques bearing the names of departed college members adorn favorite benches. My group of friends commemorated one of our lost loved ones with a tree planted in his name and recorded as such in a large book where these things are remembered. The college is literally its people. It celebrates and remembers them architecturally, in portraiture and in opportunities for students and dons. People adorn and uphold all sorts of structures at College in addition to their more obvious pedagogic and pastoral roles.

Likewise, long after we remember when and how certain things began, our family provides the architecture to support each other in values, encouragement and love. Our pictures document how my dad rests his head in his hands when it is all too much (and Hollis mirrors him). The photos visually reveal our relation to each other. Of course, the family exists beyond the photos, but a memorial in pictures helps to remind us.

Being so ill gave me time to complete the albums and it is not lost on me that they also ensure that our family memories will be organized in case I should not survive. This last was not a motivating factor, but now, newly scared about potential blood clots and strokes, I'm glad that the albums are completed, printed and on their way. Should anything happen to me, there is a record of our family life together.

Conquering the fears that arise with finding yourself on black ice requires keeping calm and steering with the motion of the car to bring it out of the slide. Turn down the bright headlights, too, and stop reading the accounts of other long haulers when such information becomes unhelpful. It is counterproductive to court PTSD and keep having to fight my way back to health. I take a deep breath and locate the inner calm again.

☙

As I approached the cottage last night at about 8:30, I was startled to see an opossum run across the road in my headlights. I braked, missed it and wondered at its presence. I hadn't remembered that opossums were in northern Michigan, although my mother has since reminded me that one got caught in our garage when I was a child. We see them frequently in Missouri. A couple of years ago, one even nestled in the lawn mower bag all winter. We found her and her young in the spring, to our mutual surprise. Opossum thus forms a link between my Interlochen and St. Louis homes at a time when my thoughts have been turning that way.

Today, I discover that Captain John Smith of the Pocahontas story is responsible for the name by which we know the opossum. In 1608, Smith described the "Apasum" (Algonquin for "white animal") as "An opossum hath a head like a Swine, and a taile like a Rate, and is of the bigness of a Cat. Under her belly she hath a bagge wherein she lodgeth, carrieth, and sucketh her young" (Wilson 256). This description sounds rather like a fanciful beast from an illuminated medieval manuscript.

There's a kernel of truth in that comparison for sightings of these odd-looking creatures are rare in this part of Michigan. I have not found

Ojibwe or Odawa stories about opossum, perhaps because these marsupials only migrated to northern lower Michigan in the 1920s, according to an article by Lisa Walsh and P.K. Tucker in the *Canadian Journal of Zoology* (108).

Among the Algonquin peoples, however, William Jones's 1907 collection of stories, *Fox Texts*, tells us of the childishly mean opossum who teased skunk when they met: "Oh, you Skunk over there, / You smell so strong that it hurts!" Opossum's words hurt Skunk, who wept in response. The black and white animal got his own back by responding, "O Opossum! a snake is following after you. / You had better look behind at your tail" (111). Opossum looked, saw that Skunk was right, and began to run away from his ostensible pursuer. Periodically, he looked back to see Snake keeping pace. After a long time, Opossum saw that Snake had stopped the chase. The running had worn out Opossum's tail and it was no longer a pretty silver.

This tale of a tail is usually understood as the comeuppance for a vain braggart; however, it also seems to be about beauty that is not at first apparent. The blinking creature in my headlights no doubt herself winced, too, as bright lights shone into nocturnal eyes. Causing discomfort was not my intent. I was as unaware of opossums in this area as we often are of black ice. Still, I was able to brake to avoid hitting her and to experience wonder that she was here.

The Algonquin parable reveals awe, too. The opossum who may appear to have an ugly tail, actually has a handsome silver tail; it's just worn out. The skunk, too, has tender feelings, not wanting to be identified with a stench. At the same time, the characters are childish pranksters. Opossum teases with playground name-calling and Skunk retaliates with a risible trick. For both, these harsh treatments of each other come out of nowhere. It is not dissimilar to the way that families and friends sometimes suddenly find themselves unable to breach differences of opinion, small jealousies or great misunderstandings. The tender mischievous child is part of human nature, as the anthropomorphic fable reminds us.

Likewise, new successes can appear out of nowhere. I did not know that Opossum was living near my home. Now, I am aware because she revealed herself in that mad dart across the road, perhaps trying to outrun her tail in the snow (or startled by the sudden light). Behind the wheel, I am shaken, but also suddenly attentive to the moment: mindful, braking and sitting still in amazement. This state – the silence of the winter road, the sudden peace after the racing heart of a near calamity, the new awareness of coexistence – this epitomizes my current journey, my arrival and my hope of continual return. Just as the opossum is found in Michigan and Missouri, it reassures me that this fresh way of being is possible wherever I call home.

OLIDAY music began earlier than usual this year. *BBC News* reported that the Philippines started listening at the beginning of September, followed by Estonia and Iceland in October, and then the UK in the first days of November (Savage). Many of my North American friends also found solace in playing holiday favorites a good two weeks before Thanksgiving. For me, it was pure joy to sing along with Hollis in the car to our Christmas CDs as we passed weathered red barns with coniferous wreaths and bright crimson bows. Driving home from evenings with my family, I now look forward to seeing holiday lights. We usually wait until December to begin our own Christmas cheer, but this year the smiling songs and merry décor are welcome relief to us in mid-November as days darken, both seasonally and in rising infections.

Traditions offer stability as they connect the passing of the year with deep-seated memories of other celebrations in better times. Without trick-or-treating, we missed our usual Halloween customs, although our family party did satisfy our little boy. Thanksgiving, in contrast, was fairly normal. Even the Macy's Thanksgiving Day Parade found a way to continue. Of course, this year's safety measures meant a shorter parade route, fewer participants, socially-distanced commentary and empty sidewalks, but there were still the familiar floats, giant balloons and performances; it was reassuringly the parade with its recognizable soundscape. Thus a comforting reminder of childhood emanated from the television while the tantalizing aroma of roasting turkey gradually strengthened.

This particular holiday embodies the spirit of our perseverance this year; we are finding a way to express thanksgiving for our blessings, even in the midst of a pandemic. It reminds me of Dr. Seuss's *The Grinch Who Stole Christmas* when the Whos in Whoville awaken on Christmas morning to the grand theft of their presents and ornaments. Yet the village still comes together to rejoice in song. The decision to celebrate and give thanks in spite of hard times is life affirming.

The US national Thanksgiving holiday originated as an effort to bring people together in the middle of the Civil War. President Abraham Lincoln declared a centralized holiday after strenuous campaigning by poet and magazine editor Sarah Josepha Hale to unite what were then different days of Thanksgiving in some states

(Norwood). The goal is laudable. However, orienting a harvest feast around the erroneous idea that there was a first Thanksgiving meal shared between Pilgrims and Indians is a dominant culture's rewriting of history and the erasure of a group's suffering.

The story buttressing the national holiday is that early European settlers learned from friendly Indians how to grow the plants that would make it possible to survive the winter. What actually happened were massacres and slave raidings by Europeans well before the *Mayflower* arrived, followed by continued bloodshed, colonization and land appropriation. David J. Silverman, author of *This Land is Their Land: The Wampanoag Indians, Plymouth Colony, and the Troubled History of Thanksgiving* (2019), writes about how Ousamequin, the Wampanoag leader, sought a strategic alliance with the Pilgrims, but not for altruistic reasons. Rather, according to Silverman:

> his people have been decimated by an epidemic disease, and Ousamequin sees the English as an opportunity to fend off his tribal rebels ... The Thanksgiving myth doesn't address the deterioration of this relationship culminating in one of the most horrific colonial Indian wars on record, King Philip's War, and also doesn't address Wampanoag survival and adaptation over the centuries, which is why they're still here, despite the odds. (Cited in Bugos)

Silverman goes on to discuss with twenty-first century Wampanoag adults what it felt like when they had experienced teachings about Thanksgiving at school. "They felt that not only their classes, but society in general was making light of historical trauma which weighs around their neck like a millstone" (cited in Bugos).

Rather than uniting all Americans in this holiday, the fictitious story solidifies a wedge between Indian country and everybody else. This harm is exactly the opposite of the sentiments purportedly celebrated in the concept of a first Thanksgiving. The idea that a genuinely friendly indigenous and settler feast really occurred only continues the colonial mindset that initiated the holiday in the first place, because it is unaware of the indignities experienced by those whose land was taken. Microaggression is often not intentional. Because the Thanksgiving story is taught as fact, many Americans unknowingly celebrate a misrepresentation and do not realize the traumatic feelings that the holiday perpetuates in its current form.

Giving thanks for all that we have during a harvest feast can still draw us together. Rather than being about Pilgrims and Indians sitting down together at Plymouth, though, we might simply celebrate people coming together. Given the deep fissures in the USA, this intentionality to talk to each other over a dinner is just as necessary today as it was in seventeenth-century Massachusetts and then again over two hundred years later when civil war divided the nation. We especially need that deliberate decision to unite in positive ways during a pandemic when we all feel isolated and sometimes afraid.

Last night, as I drove home from our harvest celebration where we expressed heartfelt thanks to be alive and together, I marveled at the rich farmland. My roots, in reconnecting to this land, make me feel more grounded in myself. The farmhouses that I pass remind me of the kitchen at my grandfather's Pennsylvania farm with the boot scraper at the front door, a large white stand-alone drainboard sink, a chin-up bar across the living room doorframe for my uncles, and a long Formica table where Grandpa would sit, sturdy and a little hunched in his denim work shirt and jeans. "I'll give you a nickel if you'll scratch my back," he'd offer my brother and me. We'd dutifully scratch the great expanse of his back with our little hands while a white plastic curved top radio played and adults conversed.

When you grow up in the country, you enjoy the same music and television shows as city cousins, but your location additionally connects with centuries-old traditions of planting, harvesting and animal husbandry. It's a funny dichotomy with the urbanity that produces entertainment and fashion for consumption in entirely different environments from its origin. I understand a little more now why my mother and her brothers have felt it to be important to communicate to their children and grandchildren the difference between hay and straw or the merits of different breeds of cattle. In a period when people wonder about the stability of the food supply, it feels luxurious to be living in a place with sandy soil and bountiful harvest for much of the year: strawberries, asparagus, cherries, blueberries, raspberries, peaches, sweet corn, apples, pumpkins, squash and maple syrup.

At the transition from now-fallow fields to forest, on the descent of mile-long Youker Hill, I look out for a trio of standing deer: three-dimensional wire yard decorations with white LED lights. They had startled me the first time that I saw them. In rural areas, without street lights and with long distances between houses, lit decorations appear now and then as cheery beacons of color in the enveloping dark. The night is otherwise broken only by the periodic warm glow of curtained windows, the steady headlights fanning out before me and, on clear nights, the moon and stars. It is so dark here without light pollution that the heavens offer quite a lot of illumination once your eyes adjust to being outside. The first time that I saw the three deer of light they appeared out of nowhere in the thick night, slightly screened by trees just off the roadside to the left. The homestead sat so much farther back in the forest that its lights were hidden from the road. With wonder and joy, I suddenly noticed these magical apparitions gleaming in the woods.

Now, tonight, it is just barely dusk. The deer decorations are lit, but they are not as stunning at twilight. About three hundred yards farther, also on the left, a brown shape stands by the roadside. Slowing the car, I peer intently, wondering if it is a wild cat. That's unlikely in this part of the world, but it is the same color as the cougar that we saw crossing the road in Banff National Park last year.

"No," I think continuing to brake softly, "not the right shape." Ah, it's a doe, standing still, gazing at the car, her wide eyes looking straight at me. My running lights are on, but in the twilight I doubt that they blind her as they would at night when her sensitive night vision suddenly encounters the flare of headlights.

At dusk, I always cautiously scan the roadsides in front for deer. They can bolt, sometimes with disastrous results for both animal and automobile. The Michigan deer that I've seen so far this year have either been crossing the road far enough ahead to pose no problem or have stood well back from the pavement. Two or three usually materialize together. This young deer, however, appears solitary. In her stillness, she simply looks intently at me. Her fine ears had probably already alerted her to my presence down the road for, in addition to the hum of the motor, "Sugar Shack" by Jimmy Gilmer and the Fireballs vibrated faintly from the speakers. Rather than bolting, the doe held her ground, head raised, waiting.

This steadfast stance seems especially remarkable given that we're at the end of deer season. She may very well have had recent, frightening experiences with loud noises. Hunting may explain her isolation if the rest of her rangale had been killed, for as matrilineal herd animals, does and fawns are inherently social. The peace in her luminous orbs remains, thankfully. Her serenity impressed me so acutely that I switched off the music; it was suddenly incongruous in the vast calm of doe eyes and wild land.

Unlike the deer statues, this living creature remains with me after the encounter, haunting with her liquid eyes, waiting at the roadside just like the two cranes of an earlier chapter. The artificial decorations are charming, but they are finally representations, not real beings. Cheerful, but predictable. I know to look for them. The true magic is the living deer who suddenly appears and looks peace into your soul. It seems fitting that the Ojibwe characterize members of the Deer Clan as pacifists who "would not even indulge in using harsh words of any kind. They were the poets of the people," Benton-Banai teaches (76).

These eye-to-eye creaturely encounters are recurring exponentially. When I was walking with the fireflies on another twilight evening in mid-July, my footfall startled a mother and baby raccoon. They raced up two trees, the mother hiding behind the trunk. The kit was curious, however, and clung to the side of the tree, peeping at me and watching curiously as I returned its contemplation. Then during the month between mid-October and now, cranes, chipmunk and deer all followed the direct gaze of the small raccoon and steadfastly looked me in the eye.

A couple weeks ago, a black squirrel clung upside down on a tree trunk at eye level about two feet away and likewise held my gaze. I grew up with the ubiquitous black squirrel and the less populous grey. The encounter a fortnight ago was highly unusual. The squirrel's ease was reflected in a quiet tail; normally squirrels flick their tails in warning when human beings are near. Here, though, was an ebony eye, a small bright bead assessing me while little paws energetically clung upside down. Then the little creature gracefully sidled around the trunk, smoothly hiding, like the well-mannered exit of a practiced host excusing himself to mingle with other guests. It felt impossible to look again for Squirrel without rudeness.

Within the same population group, these energetic rodents are social beings. To human observers, they appear to be jolly workers, finding and stashing nuts for the winter in scampering play. Every morning, I open the green and white botanical-print curtains and have a cuppa tea in bed, grinning at the antics of black squirrels chasing each other. Psychedelic Squirrels, more recent Interlochen Arts Academy students have named them. Their agile leaps along overhead branches seem easy arboreal gambols, rather than difficult gymnastics on a series of springy tightropes. Then they stand still to nibble acorns, little paws busily working. Or they watch us watching them, tail warily flicking, keeping their distance. As they squirrel away nuts in multiple underground cellars, they seem perfectly to balance prudence with play.

For me, anxious about how to achieve exactly that approach, it seems that squirrels are able to master more than the usual concept of work/life balance. As the upside-down squirrel and I placidly exchanged gazes, I realized how creatures-watching-humans differs dramatically from humanity's second-order surveillance, where a person adjusts his or her conduct under the awareness of being under observation by overseers, peers and oneself (through an internalization of social norms). Often, we are not conscious of being watched by wildlife. Their gaze does not exert the same sort of behavioral control on us; rather, their fear causes them to flee, as mama raccoon did at the height of summer. When animals do hold our gaze, it is as equals who communicate through their eyes, as baby raccoon, chipmunk, deer and squirrel had done when they stood calmly and let mutual sight travel the path between our eyes. This non-judgmental exchange differs from the surveillance that underpins many aspects of human societies, including how we work and how we try to heal (in hospitals' architectural structures and therapy's talking cure, as the first chapter discusses).

It is an honor when a wild creature recognizes the inner stillness in a person. Such calm allows both individuals simply to witness each other's presence (our being here, now, together) before we just as easily move on. Thus two creatures reflect to each other an openness and a willingness. When you think of the wary conditioning of animals in relationship to *Homo sapiens*, it is truly remarkable to think of a person's ability to be so non-threating that this approachability can happen. There is no fear in our encounter; Squirrel, noticeably, did not swish its tail as it disappeared. Rather, there is perhaps curiosity at encountering a human with inner serenity, who looks back with respect. Together, we stand, gaze into each other's eyes and find a marvelous world offered, because we are both at peace.

This type of interaction with animals exemplifies the ancient Chinese concept of *wu wei*, which roughly means self-control and inaction. "The way to do is to be," is a more familiar way of putting it. *Wu wei* is an attitude of being, not an act. It obtains its ends by attraction instead of compulsion. This recalls the modern disease of disconnection that I mentioned in Chapter 10. COVID-19 is providing opportunities to achieve *wu wei*, or to connect with the natural world and each other, without overworking. This connectivity is evinced when beings approach or present themselves to you.

The three great qualities of the Tao (way) are: compassion/love, frugality/moderation and humility. As it wends toward conclusion, the *Tao Te Ching* exemplifies *wu wei* in practice:

> The whole world says that my way is vast and resembles nothing. It is because it is vast that it resembles nothing. If it resembled anything, it would, long before now, have become small.
> I have three treasures
> Which I hold and cherish.
> The first is known as compassion,
> The second is known as frugality,
> The third is known as not daring to take the lead in the empire;
> ...
> What heaven succours it protects with the gift of compassion.
>
> (LXVII, 163–4, 165)

To my way of thinking, the animals sense compassion, moderation and humility. This attitude honors who they are as beings in their own rights. It is what the *Tao* calls "the mysterious virtue": "In concentrating your breath [life] can you become as supple / As a babe?" (X, 26, 24). Put another way, can you become innocent, returning to your roots?

This process requires a balancing of our two types of spirit. In acupuncture, the *po* of the lungs and the *hun* of the liver are considered two different souls: the first attached to the bones and returning to earth after death, and the second ethereal, surviving after death. Maciocia tells us that because the Chinese pictograms for *po* and *hun* contain the character of *gui* (the soul of a dead person), they are understood to have that aspect of a spirit which is an independent existence, always in motion. Thus Section X of the *Tao Te Ching* begins:

> When carrying on your head your perplexed bodily soul can you
>   embrace in your arms the One
> And not let go? (24)

Returning to my childhood home and resting in the woods has enabled a repair of my psyche. It has uncoupled the "perplexed" from the "bodily soul" (the *po* of the lungs) and allowed me to heal the liver – the *hun* of ethereal movement – the part of me that is connected to the way itself. My questions at present pertain to how to return to the world and to continue to balance internally, so that I can maintain the inner silence or the return to a natural state. Yoga and meditation also facilitate the feeling of vast inner space. Can I bring together the "bodily soul" with the mysterious virtue of these ancient ways? "When your discernment penetrates the four quarters / Are you capable of knowing anything?" (Tzu, X, 24). The four quarters are perceived as the compass directions or as fire, water, metal and wood, with earth at the center. Once I have healed enough to return to work, can I find a way of maintaining this whole person balance of mind/body/spirit that is encapsulated by the idea of knowing while also retaining natural quiet, or the not-knowing of innocence? Will the animals still feel my calm and seek mutual communication?

ꙮ

Three days later, I awoke to snow dusting the ground and the wind gusting. As I walked along the conservancy bluff, I could clearly see waves far below. The storm blew so hard that it sounded like ongoing static along the shoreline, punctuated with occasional surges. The brittle leaves crackled underfoot while little pings of snow forcefully hit them.

My cheeks burned, too, from the pin pricks of snow blown against my face. The air felt pure, perhaps from the negative ions created by the pounding waves and whipping tree limbs.

I particularly admired the tall canopies of the large dominant trees that provide protection to the surrounding seedlings. In February 2020, journalist Andrew Nikiforuk paraphrased biologist Diana Beresford-Kroeger's hypothesis "that mother trees wear a fragrant apron of chemicals that attracts all kinds of life." Admitting that science does not yet understand much that she has observed, Beresford-Kroeger names them "epicenter trees. They invite the birds and insects. It is like there is a call from the tree and maybe the birds hear it" (cited in Nikiforuk).

There's a mother tree at the start of the boardwalk to the lake. I call it the Three Sisters because its thick girth divides into three trunks above my head. One curves slightly, mirroring the twist in the hillside stairs. When I first took the cats down to the lake on their leashes, they both stopped here and, with great stillness, slowly, looked up at Three Sisters, following the line of the trunk with their eyes, up into the canopy, as if in salutation. Recently, I have been greeting this majestic white pine myself with a pause and a silent humble, "Thank you, tree" of appreciation. Sometimes, I spread my fingers on its rough bark to connect more viscerally.

White pines rise high over the forest in vast, bushy greens that today sweep around so forcefully that I halfway expect the torque to twist and spiral their mighty trunks in front of me. These white pines nevertheless remain stately straight. They're a good analogy for how the body can wave with the perplexity of emotions or difficult thoughts, while the spirit embraces the source of energy, bending without breaking. The inside remains serene as seen by the tree's upright, quiet return when the wind stops.

It is true hibernation time now. The air feels distinctly different from even a couple days ago. With each breath, cold air sucks into the lungs, sharp like an internal cleanse. It feels good. The chipmunks curl warm in their winter dens. They disappeared on the night that I spied the deer while driving home. Our black bear should be sinking into her winter sleep, too, her hormones triggered by the decrease in daylight. She was last seen by Candace six days before Thanksgiving, bulked up for dormancy. Today, even the squirrels and birds remain in their nests. The squirrels who internalize that work/play balance don't keep up their preparations on a blustery day; rather, they cuddle in their treetop nests, rocked by the tempest lullaby.

It is time for rest. Living in a cabin in the woods, the attunement to the natural world includes a fresh sort of tiredness. Unlike the fatigue of illness or sleep deprivation, this heaviness is dreamlike. My ongoing inner state is close to the meditative movement that I've achieved in the past when I've started my day with Ashtanga yoga.

We might think about this state in psychological terms as existing at the top of the vagus or pneumogastric nerve. This nerve runs the length of the body and interfaces with heart, lung and digestive track control as well as with "neck, throat, eyes, and ears." Psychologists understand that a person is not only healthy when experiencing the ventral vagal state, but also that thinking remains most cogent in it. People operating thus are creative, relaxed, social, open to new things, curious, and compassionate toward self and others (Dana 8, 27). It is the place that I find when in nature or while writing. Stimulating the vagus nerve, and therefore transitioning from either a "fight or flight" or a "freeze or faint" response, can occur through movement. Mind/body practices like yoga, t'ai chi and qigong are excellent for activating the ventral vagal state, as are calming walks in nature.

This state of being is what animals seem to recognize. Now when I'm out walking and meet a neighbor with a skittish red bloodhound, the dog shows curiosity rather than fear to me. I'm the only person to engender this response, his person volunteers. Animals know.

This ventral vagal state supports health. Social worker Deb Dana, in imaging the autonomic nervous system as a ladder that we scale or descend as we feel safe or endangered, places it at the top. In contrast, she informs us that various serious physical problems arise from sustained existence at the middle of the ladder. Once a feeling of unease triggers the need for action (flight or fright), we enter a pathway of response that can lead to "heart disease; high blood pressure; high cholesterol; sleep problems; weight gain; memory impairment; headache; chronic neck, shoulder, and back tension; stomach problems; and an increased vulnerability to illness." The repercussions for more extremely shutting down while operating in the dorsal vagal state at the bottom of the ladder include inactivity on multiple levels: physical, digestive, cognitive, energetic and emotional. Health consequences "can include chronic fatigue, fibromyalgia, stomach problems, low blood pressure, type 2 diabetes, and weight gain" (Dana 11-12). For me, that's motivation enough for another stroll in the woods.

CℬℬↃ

Till and I went walking today on a wildlife path by the water's edge. His new harness, florescent orange with a reflective strip to match, clashes with his ginger fur. Deer season ended four days previously, but management of waterfowl and rodents is ongoing. I frequently see rusty brown pickup trucks and dusty black SUVs parked near forest access points, often with orange-vested hunters gathering their gear to set forth. Although they are not supposed to hunt in the conservancy, it is almost impossible to distinguish boundary lines in the wild and therefore it's necessary to take precautions, like Till's vest and my orange armbands.

As Till and I ambled between the cottage and a lake access path, dried leaves glistened as the morning sun reflected off a thin sheen of ice coating each surface. Even the sand was brittle, crackling, crick-cracking underfoot instead of shifting fluidly as in summer. When we reached lakeside, the lapping water softened the sand along the shore.

Till loves to explore new paths and he took me on an unexpected adventure at the lakeshore. Somehow, he knew to trot along the beach for a little while, so lightly as not to mark the sand like the deer hooves had done earlier. Both deer prints and Till turned inland on a wildlife path that hides among long grasses in the summer. I had never seen it before. I followed the tug of Till's leash, guided by both it and the traces of deer. The trail ascended through a paper birch grove and along a shallow sandbar where the grasses wedge out into the lake. Here, buzzing water insects enlivened the air to the accompaniment of the rustle of dry leaves overhead and the papery rattle of the water grass.

Suddenly, two bald eagles launch themselves into the sky from a giant white pine, slow wings belying the speed of such powerful, sweeping pinioned stretches. Eagles usually fly alone, but here are two crisscrossing each other and interweaving as they ascend over the lake, sun gleaming on white crowns and tails. Astonished and awestruck, I freeze in wonder.

Their erstwhile perch is part of a mystical, primeval landscape of eastern red cedars, gnarled into fantastic shapes, knees breaking the ground, roots showing as trunks stretch parallel with the lake. Alongside, reeds arch under the weight of ice, frozen into miniature cathedrals and fairy wings. Ginger pine needles carpet the forest floor. No fallen leaves here, just the striped grey bark of cedar, their majestic green swags and juniper heavily scenting the air. The essential oils smell naturally pharmaceutical and so beautifully aromatic that it encourages deep breathing.

Unsurprisingly, the Ojibwe medicine wheel features cedar. Its quadrant is connected with the south, with summer and with the trickster Coyote, or Nanabozho, Nanbizho, Manabazho or Winabojo, as this legendary character is variously called. He outwitted enemies and taught the Anishinaabek how to live in the wild, according to ethnomusicologist Frances Densmore, including instructing them in medicinal remedies. Nanabozho wore cedar ornamentally as a sort of headdress, with its roots descending around him (381, 385). Along with sage, sweetgrass and tobacco, cedar is used ceremonially because it is believed to link "our primary memories and our deepest creature selves to the highest spiritual aspects of our humanity" (Savinelli 18).

Cedar's growth appears otherworldly, too, with the elder trees' wizened trunks growing at crooked angles and their knees breaking the earth's surface as if the tree is in motion. Notably, this stretch of cedar grows next to a grove of paper birch – the "two most sacred trees of the Ojibwe, both of which are so useful to them" (Smith 414). Besides the bark being used for buckets, baskets, waterproof roofs for wigwams, patterns for artwork, and the keeping of "medicine lodge ritual," Huron H. Smith tells us that paper birch "root bark and maple sugar cooked together made a soothing syrup to alleviate cramps in the stomach" (414, 358). It occurs to me that canoe building would be easier in this spot, too, because of the juxtaposition of the birch and cedar copses: the latter provided the ribs of birchbark canoes.

After observing each element in isolation in earlier chapters, many are beginning to come together now. The trees, lake, earth; the peace of deer; the work/life balance of squirrels; the medicinal and messenger eagles; and the sacred cedar with its trickster coyote association. Nature's love emerges from a rich biodiversity that helps all its creatures, including *Homo sapiens*, to live intuitively and respectfully, with compassion and humility. Request nature's assistance, watch closely, and help will come. Professor Suzanne Simard, the scientist who discovered how trees in a forest are linked through mycorrhizal networks, posits that if trees are so sensitive that they "sense nearby plants and animals and alter their behavior accordingly," then they may very well perceive us, too (Jabr).

As my feline friend and I walk among the ancient cedar alongside this lake of water lingering, it seems to me that my dreamy state feels lethargic because it contrasts with what had been my *modus operandi:* a stressed-out adrenaline rush operating at the middle of the autonomic nervous system ladder: the need to accomplish things and to do so immediately. In contrast, I now feel in a flow state that accesses the unconscious.

This harmony with nature is conceptualized in Taoism as *p'u*, or primal simplicity and a natural self. The *Tao Te Ching* counsels water-like behavior and awareness of the relativity of all attributes. There is no competition in a healthy body. *P'u* feels desireless, selfless, unassertive. The ability to achieve this state partially comes from existing within a larger healthy organism, which makes it possible to live without effort, like water. "In a home it is the site that matters," counsels the *Tao Te Ching*, "In an ally it is benevolence that matters; / ... / In government it is order that matters" (VIII, 21). Without a doubt, we are better able to achieve our best selves when our relationships are benevolent and ordered. I am particularly drawn to the idea of thinking about where to situate a home. In today's market, this idea usually means that neighborhood helps to determine the economic value of a house. Thinking in terms of *p'u*, however, means that a site that supports healthy states is most valuable, from being able to see something natural like a tree offering its shade to being located away from avalanche zones and flood plains.

Extending this idea of *p'u* in terms of traditional Chinese medicine, we might think of the individual energies (heart, kidney, spleen, lungs and liver) and how they relate to form the whole self. In fact, at the next acupuncture session after the above realizations, I was startled to find that my liver points, which had been the focus of our treatments, no longer needed attention. Rather, my heart point was speaking up. I had previously been too sensitive for needling at this acupuncture point. The other, individual organs needed treatment first. Now I was ready to bring them all together and treat the *shen* of the full spirit.

Walking here, on this forested lakeshore, I think of the rich humus beneath my feet, the lethargy with which my toes and heels sink deep into this coniferous topsoil, through lush moss and cedar roots like Nanabozho gathering the tree around him. Above me, my intuitions rise like fingertips reaching toward the heaven to join the eagles. These mighty warriors symbolize the strength and courage for new beginnings: doubly so, for I had seen a monogamous pair sky-dancing together. Humanity occupies the medial state between earth and sky, lengthening toward both.

Standing awestruck on this turmeric turf – this is always the way to be. The idea of work/life balance is itself misleading because it suggests a binary. The squirrel is true to its nature because it integrates work and play. The feeling of dreamy dormancy can exist in all areas of life as a continuum. This ventral vagal level connects to biodiversity in plant and animal life; it is social in a way that exists beyond logic and words. These deep, natural energies integrate the person, too, supporting mind, body and spiritual health. They endow daily life with wonder and mystery, simply because we look more attentively at nature.

Having discovered the properties of cedar, I am motivated to know more about the other trees in the vicinity. My attention has thus far been taken up with the white and red pines, and the oak and maple that mostly populate the forest, including directly outside of the cottage. Two windows at the side of the living room, however, look out on draping hemlock boughs (*Tusuga canadensis*). This tree "has long been used in North America by the aboriginal peoples as an emergency food source, in the treatment of fevers, colds, sore throats, general infections, and rheumatism, as haemolytic agents, and in the management of various venereal diseases," Beresford-Kroeger tells us in *Arboretum America*. "The Ojibwa peoples used the bark of *T. canadensis*, which is very high in tannic acid, to heal open wounds and to stop the bleeding" (170). I thankfully observe the hemlock growing at the side of our cottage, now attaching healing meaning to this gorgeous tree, along with a nonlinguistic sense of its individual being. It's like getting to know one's neighbors better.

Similarly, because I was talking more about trees, my dad observed that the view from the cottage into the conservancy includes a tamarack tree, or American larch (*Larix laricina*), which thrives in swampy conditions. The only deciduous pine in Michigan, the tamarack's needles turn golden before falling off. "The Moral of the Tamarack's Fall from Grace" is an Ojibwe legend about how Chickadee beseeched the tamarack to offer it shelter from snow and wind, but in its vanity, the tree refused to wrap its beautiful branches around the frozen little bird. An ancient pine, however, lowered its branches protectively because it had experienced such cold before. The Creator punished the tamarack tree, resulting in its autumnal shed. The pine, in contrast, retained its needles because of its kindness. This fable teaches the lesson of compassion.

Such stories can lead to birdwatching, as experienced by the young Ojibwe man who told this story of Tamarack in the pages of the *Calgary Herald:* "traditional stories exist for the listener to journey back to again and again." This process led him to birding:

> I began to see differences in their rhythms, their attitudes and, of course, in their plumage and their songs. But the biggest thing I noticed was the change that happened in me when I took the time to see them ...
>
> When they sang, I heard the voice of celebration, of the benevolence of life, of grace and mercy.

We need this song of celebration, especially when life seems its darkest and coldest.

Nature can exist quite prominently in our daily space, but remain unseen as we bustle around. We can find our way to it through taking time to notice. During the pandemic, more people have spontaneously taken up birding, according to the *Audubon Magazine*. Starting in April 2020 when life became slower with lockdowns, people suddenly saw the birds in their own backyards (Dhanesha; Cosier). Nature had always been there, looking in our windows. With the pandemic, we are simply looking back.

"O brave new world," Miranda exclaims in Shakespeare's *The Tempest.*

"'Tis new to thee," Prospero dryly replies (V.i.185, 186).

And so we return to the beginning: What if long COVID has saved lives?

Our harvest feast thus offers thanks for what we have: the bounty of nature and the aspects of healing that send us individually and collectively to our roots in nature. It includes being truly seen for who we are (not what we do) by the deer standing beside the road or the squirrel hanging upside down on the tree, along with a person being aware enough to look back. This process takes us forward, like the loyal eagle pair launching themselves together toward a fresh place and jubilantly interlacing their journeys on their way. As the narrator so aptly puts it in the novel that Olive Schreiner published in 1883, *The Story of an African Farm:*

And now we turn to Nature. All these years we have lived beside her, and we have never seen her; and now we open our eyes and look at her. (151)

I awoke to a landscape transformed on December 12th. Periodically during the night, soft thuds of wet snow fell on the roof as a heavy rain transitioned to a proper snow. It's so quiet in the forest. Light through the tall gabled window high over my bed reveals pine boughs encrusted with snow, their heaviness forming a stationary lace. The mostly bare branches of an oak creak and sway above, a few hardy leaves clinging and fluttering against the white sky.

When I opened the curtains and scrambled quickly back to bed, I observed an unfamiliar world. The trees no longer looked like old friends, but rather seemed to be new beings with snow lining the full length of their lakeside trunks, leaving black-grey ribbons of bark exposed on the other side, each tree striped half and half. Snow capped the surfaces of leafless branches and lined each pine needle. Because of their dark undersides, the tines stood in relief against the snowy ground and the distant white where the sky intermittently peeked through.

A static seems to flicker across the scene as flakes steadily float down at a forty-five degree angle, the wind causing a tiny red pine, two feet tall, to duck its head and sway, like an agreeable supplicant. Springy branches overhead belie the weight of new snow, bobbing as horses do in harness. With a toss of their heads, a whinny from these equine boughs would not surprise me. But all is quiet except for the trees moving, tiny snowflakes falling and a black squirrel nimbly leaping across an enormous log. Till is curled up at my feet and Arya is on my lap, both as fast asleep as the world.

The silence of the forest with its soporific, heavy movement reminds me of the calm pond, the symbol of the healthy spirit. Its quality of emptiness (silence), simultaneous with gentle movement, evokes the lines from the *Tao Te Ching* with which Chapter 8 closed: "I do my utmost to attain emptiness / I hold firmly to stillness" (XVI, 37). In doing so, I find space to grow and move. This inner state is like a vase that creates negative or empty space: "Knead clay in order to make a vessel. Adapt the nothing therein to the purpose in hand, and you will have the use of the vessel" (XI, 27). Our society normally focuses on the vessel itself and its design qualities: shape, color, material, decoration and place of origin. Taoism, however, contemplates the inside of the vessel and how it creates a "nothing," or a void that makes it useful. "Thus what we gain is Something, yet it is by virtue of Nothing that this can be put to use" (XI, 27a).

The silence of winter is deeply calming. This emptiness contains the purring cat on my lap as I write. The overall quality is an enduring serenity that feels complete and happy, unlike the rush of modern life with its constant quest to fill the inner void through doing, having and being more. That materialism is insatiable, for as soon as we have the thing for which we longed, we are already consumed with our next desire. In contrast, the peace of a winter morning in the woods is satisfying. There is no need to fill it, but instead it comprises the simple fact of being here and now with the snow, the cats and a mug of tea. "The way is empty, yet use will not drain it" (Tzu IV, 11). Watching and being, seeing anew and enjoying what is: these are the roots of a healthy, whole person.

Mother nature, in now emphasizing the long line of the trees with a chiaroscuro of white against charcoal grey, changes the trees' summer and autumn rhythm. The trunks appear more slender while they simultaneously support the stripes of vertical snow, or the reach of frozen water between pristine earth and white sky. No wonder I find myself smiling as I write. This quiet world, this peace, inspires a song of thanksgiving and blessing. This particular forest had to seed itself again at the turn of the century after the Douglas and Buckley Lumber Company of Manistee cut the old-growth white cedar and processed it at the Wylie Cooperage Company, just north of the state park. A forest fire ensued when loggers left behind dead branches and leaves. My healing has thus occurred in synergy with the forest's own spirit of renewal.

Do I, then, awake to a transformed world or, rather, does my response to its snowy transfiguration indicate my own change? We might view the self as comprising four circles radiating out, with the inner two focused on aspects of the inner self and the outer two on the self in relation to the external world. The configuration reminds me of the annual growth rings in a tree trunk and helps me to reassess my own journey.

My first, tentative steps in the innermost aspect of self (*yin wei mai*) included childhood memories of being held in the water, thoughts about the nuances of walking, and feelings of being situated in the deep unconsciousness of the sleeping bear. Then two chapters on education ("Coyote" and "The Ha-Ha") preceded an increasing attention to animals who are guides and messengers, ending with my sense of how I think of self (*yang wei mai*) as integrated with awe-inspiring natural energies, whether at work or at play. This wild world is just outside the window. It is by being calm in nature and observing that we can attain a similar, deeply satisfying internal quiet.

This awareness signals a turn to *yin qiao mai*, or that extraordinary vessel that is oriented more to the external world than the inward *wei* vessels. While the Chinese character for *qiao* "refers to a tightening and loosening of muscles, most commonly in the legs," the *yin-yang* vessel interplay is best understood as coordination anywhere in the body: "when one muscle tightens, another must loosen to provide free range of movement" (Wang 291). Besides walking and other multiple, complex muscle coordinations, *yin* and *yang qiao mai* also have to do with eye functions, both awake and asleep. Because the *yin qiao mai* is associated with channels in the leg that travel to facial movement, as well as with "the movement of muscles in and around the internal organs" (Wang 291), there are synergies with anatomical understandings of the vagus nerve, which the previous chapter discussed as having to do with involuntary control of the heart, lungs and digestive track along with the face and throat. In this sense, *yin qiao mai* might be said to be that aspect of self that orients a person in a certain way. It has to do with inner and outer sight as connected to nourishing the ventral vagal state: calm, cogent and socially connected. After that, only *yang qiao mai* remains, which might be thought of as springing forth to take action in the world because it is *yang* (vital, active, stimulating). I suspect this last will occur outside these pages; it will be the process of returning to work and of sharing *The Arrow Tree* with you.

છ૪ૐ

With the snowstorm I am newly oriented. I find my feet working harder than they do when traversing unpaved summer paths. My route today lies over the same ground, but this now-unfamiliar topography requires my feet to sink through wet snow and lift, ankles to rock over unseen gradations and fallen branches, and legs to clench to avoid slipping. It's hard going. The uneven terrain requires muscles to shift with the unpredictability. In a couple days, packed tire and snowmobile tracks on unplowed roads will be first welcomed and then avoided as they turn treacherous with ice.

From growing up here, I'm used to the trick of slightly drawing up the knee muscles to brace on a slick winter surface. Children from the north naturally learn the shuffle-walk required for slippery ground. As a teen, I could usually go full winters without falling, even on the slippery hill leading, ironically, to the dance studio at Interlochen Arts

Academy. We students became adept at slide-gliding down the curved slope to the flat bridge that led to the front door, wiping feet and stamping off the snow as we entered. Muscle memory proves reliable again now, even as the malaise of recent illness places minute exertion into the foreground of consciousness.

What feels unique is the effort to orient a newly reclaimed self to a world that has assumed a novel, snowy guise. My eyes are tired from trying to take in all the nuance. The branches, each perfectly outlined in white and grey-black, overwhelm me in a forest of detail. The wood and leaves no longer blur together in a mutual camouflage. Rather, everything in this exquisite world seems to require attention. I'm reminded of the 3D quality of first recognizing the animate wild (Chapter 4) when the trees seemed to crowd toward me in eager assistance and pleasure at being recognized and acknowledged.

It is bewildering to feel out in the world again, like blinking in the brightness of a Michigan winter where recent snow flashes and sparkles in sunshine on a soft snow-ground. Over the boardwalk to the lake, branches from the surrounding Michigan holly bush and tag alder arch so low under their snowy burdens that passage is almost impossible. I bow low, too, with arched back echoing the tunnel overhead as I bend my way through to the other side. This, too, is a humble, careful orientation of self within the world around me. Again, such uneven terrain has the effect of a mindful alignment of self to this very quiet place.

On all sides, heavily-laden pine boughs droop with snow like icing. A black squirrel makes me grin as he plunges down a maple head first, on the snowy side. The snow sprinkles his head as he descends, but his path is clear when he climbs the tree again on the same side. Why did Squirrel do that?

Our cat offers a clue when I take him out for a walk three days later. Till has been desperate to go out ever since the winter storm. He's been meowing repeatedly to me, the neat little line of his front bottom teeth showing each time he makes his request. When I took him out the day after the snowfall, he disliked sinking to the top of his leg with each step. It was his first encounter with snow. Today, a little of the white ground covering has melted and enough people have trodden the path to make a firm surface. I carry Till wrapped in a warm towel to the lake. With each breaking wave, irregular plates of ice jangle against each other, sounding like wooden windchimes. Till communicates with his wriggles that he wants down for investigative purposes. Slowly, we walk and watch the sapphire lake, brilliant blue against the white birch trees lining the snowy shore.

As we wend our way back, slowly so that Till can pick his way along the footprints, he suddenly races ahead and up a white oak. About twelve feet up, he grasps around the trunk in a hug and is clearly surprised that his right paw slips in the snow along that side of the bark. It alarms him and he doesn't attempt to climb another tree during our outing.

Ever since Till discovered that he could climb trees about a month ago, our strolls have been more like tree climbing expeditions. We walk along, Till pausing at the base of oaks and maples to look slowly up the trunk in inspection, or to sniff the base and then gaze toward the canopy. He is getting to know each individual tree, but is probably also picking up an array of sensory information that is unavailable to *Homo sapiens*. At other times, he takes a running start and scampers right up the trunk, clinging five to ten feet up, before shuffling down and then making a final spring to the ground.

Our Till, climbing a snow-encrusted tree only to have his paw slip, offers an explanation for Squirrel's behavior. The latter's snowplow down the trunk cleared the way for future climbing. It was a safety maneuver so that he could gambol up whichever side was needed to hide from alarming creatures such as Till and myself. As a veteran forest dweller, the fluffy-tailed *sciuridae* (the small rodent family) had experience with slippery trunks, but Till had to learn for himself.

It is not unlike beginning to emerge again to the working world. I am not yet back to work, but I have needed to be in contact with the university world in advance of the spring semester. Communications begin to surface regarding how universities across the USA are making decisions in the wake of COVID-related fiscal loss. Their decisions will impact the advancement of knowledge in numerous fields, especially in the arts and humanities, which bear the greatest burden of cuts, reorganizations and increased teaching loads. Yet the arts and humanities have been essential components in my recovery of mind/body health. Making and enjoying music, literature, film, dance and visual art have, in fact, made life bearable for millions of people during severe illness, international emergency and social isolation. Undoubtedly, we need STEM subjects (Science, Technology, Engineering, Math), but we also need to nurture the creative spirit and continue to advance our understanding of what it means to be human. Moreover, a colleague recently observed to me that it's a false binary to separate some of these disciplines into the arts and humanities only; certain aspects of music, for example, clearly have STEM elements.

I feel my own paws slipping. How do we engage with this world when the economic situation is so dire? Employers are justifiably trying to stay afloat and to protect jobs. Vast numbers of people are now unemployed or struggling financially. Yet overwork is not the answer, for workplace imbalance leads to stress-related disease and loss of the core self.

Perhaps we need to learn a different gait. A couple days ago, I was able to cross-country ski in the new powder that fell on top of the original wet snowfall. The conditions were perfect. The swishing sound and rhythmic slide go back to deepest childhood, for I was cross-country skiing soon after I could walk. Cross-country skiing is a vigorous, full-body work-out and I carefully kept my outing to ten minutes. I paused several times to look over the lacy branches in the foreground to the white lake beyond. Afterwards, I could feel the muscular use, but was exuberant to realize that there was no post-exertional malaise, just a healthy appetite and a good night's sleep. Maybe instead of trying to remain upright by walking on snowy and icy surfaces, we need to remember that skiing, skating and snowshoeing are sometimes options. Gaits can change with the season.

I need a new relation to my job more than ever given COVID-related stresses within the workplace. My future task will be to balance holistic, intuitive health with my gravitation to intellectual research, writing and teaching. I suppose the best orientation is to observe the trees, who have faced threats of deforestation, fire, lightning and disease. The wood outside my window is peopled with individual and interconnected coniferous and deciduous trees. If I can concentrate on continually returning to a sense of being as integrated with the natural world, and varying my posture and pace as needed, then I believe that my orientation will remain holistic. Finding inner stillness allows one to shift with challenges because it maintains a relaxed stance. The focus is not on the doing, but rather on the being. Reside in the inner calm and enjoy the vibrant strength of the wild.

(3&)

Waking with wonder at the world, today is quiet with a new dusting of snow. The frozen white of winter looks almost blue in the first hour of dawn. The ground and the white stripes of snow on the tree trunks glow slightly in this baby-blue light, all quiet except for the purr of the furnace and the early foraging of a black squirrel close to the cottage. This mystic hour offers the purest form of a meditation like medication. In a hibernating stillness, the qualities of the unconscious mind can shape the day. Rather than awakening to the hurry-scurry of a mind already on the go, consumed with thoughts of work and worry, the opposite can occur: inner peace can structure our orientation to external life. Doing so enables one similarly to shape the world with these qualities, rather than with the storminess of inner flurries.

There are true cultural crises emerging in the wake of Pandemic '20-21. How we position ourselves relative to them will have long-reaching consequences for ourselves and our communities. In relatively recent history, societies tend to increase overwork when jobs become scarce. We were already headed in this direction before the subprime mortgage crisis sent the country and then the world into the Great Recession (December 2007-June 2009 USA; 2009 globally). It was then the largest economic crisis since the Great Depression of the 1930s. Workplace trends just before 2007, however, suggest that we were already on track for placing less value on the holistic self even before the brokerage firm Lehman Brothers declared bankruptcy in September 2008 and sent the Dow Jones Industrial Average into a downward spiral. With the Great Recession, universities witnessed dramatically fewer parents guiding their children toward arts and humanities subjects, favoring instead what were thought to be high-salaried STEM fields. This public perception does not match reality, however, as reported by Scott Carlson in a 2018 article for *The Chronicle of Higher Education*, "Over Time, Humanities Grads Close the Pay Gap with Professional Peers."

Because it is generally thought that the recession beginning in 2020 will exceed the Great Recession, it may be useful to think about how the worker has fared within a larger sweep of history. In 2005 and 2006, an alarming workplace trend was reported by news agencies around the world. On Labor Day weekend 2006, the *NBC Nightly News* observed that so many Americans did not take their full holiday days that if you were to average out the amount over the entire working population, then each person gave back four days of paid holiday time to the employer in 2006. Moreover, our northern neighbors were doing the same, albeit not quite as much. In September 2005, *CBC News* found that of the twenty-one annual vacation days typically given to Canadians, "The average employee gives up three vacation days a year, according to research carried out by Ipsos-Reid Canada." "Vacation Deprivation" only continued to increase, according to Ipsos-Reid in an article of that name. By March 2008, 29% of Canadians were not taking their full vacation time, up eight points from the previous year.

Why was this happening even before the Great Recession? The CBC article title, "Survey: Canadians Skip Vacation, Fear Falling Behind at Work," says it all. North Americans live in fear. We worry that promotions, if not job security, are threatened if we take extended time off to connect in a meaningful way with our families and ourselves. Stephanie Rosenbloom concurs in her article for *The New York Times* called "Please Don't Make Me Go on Vacation," before going on to cite a 2005 Families and Work Institute study which found that even when people are away from the office, one fifth are not really "away." Modern technology facilitates working and keeping in contact. Rosenbloom additionally paraphrases the president of the Families and Work Institute, Ellen Galinsky, as identifying the root problem as lying in: "Downsizing, labor market volatility and the country's shift from an industrial economy to one based on service and knowledge." The result? People expect immediate responses to e-mails, "vacation or no vacation," and more readily cross the boundaries between work and leisure time.

One night in the late 1990s, I remember my father telling us at the dinner table about some crucial decision that was going forward regarding the architectural design for the new library building at Interlochen Center for the Arts. My parents were both involved since Dad directed the music library and Mom directed the academic library. Dad had bumped into the chair of the design committee and informed him of the family vacation dates. With disbelief, Dad reported that the chair had asked about e-mail access. "No, we'll be on vacation," my dad replied. Now, twenty-some years later, I find it virtually impossible to make the same firm statement. When did work encroach on non-contractual hours and expect the employee to pay for it?

Rosenbloom's humorous title, "Please Don't Make Me Go on Vacation," unfortunately echoes current workplace attitudes held not only by employees, but also by employers. Even more ironically, the articles that I perused make the point that we *must* vacation in order to work effectively. Two or three days sprinkled hither and thither are ineffective for true rejuvenation; we require at least two days to begin to unwind before true rest can commence. In other words, rather than concentrating on what we lose in our lives by never leaving the office, the reports justify time off because it allows workers to refresh themselves in ways that make people, and by extension the workplace, most productive. Human beings are thus imagined as cogs in a machine.

Rather than continuing to accept this shared value system, perhaps we should investigate its pressures, supposed ideals, actual outcomes and origins. CBC cites Benjamin Hunnicutt, a historian of labor and professor of leisure studies at University of Iowa, as saying that we now find our self-definition and a sense of life meaning through work, not through our leisure. We approach work as a new religion, Hunnicutt argues (*Kellogg's* 24).

It is helpful to understand the relevant social and political shifts that brought Western society to this pass. Hunnicutt explores in his books,

Work without End and *Kellogg's Six-Hour Day*, how Britain and America experienced a movement in the nineteenth and early twentieth centuries to increase wages and reduce working hours with the goal of bettering human lives. The result was tangible and widespread.

Similar ideas were at the fore of my own thinking in 2006 as I was readying a book for publication that year. *The Musical Crowd in English Fiction, 1840–1910: Class, Culture and Nation* explores how the formation of working-class musical culture went hand-in-hand with improvements in health, safety and working hours. In the middle of the British nineteenth century, laboring people suddenly had the time and surplus capital to enjoy the corresponding growth in leisure activities, including sports, community music-making, concert attendance, adult education and seaside resorts, to name a few. The importance of leisure time is also treated in a book that I published more recently in 2017, *Mary Gladstone and the Victorian Salon: Music, Literature, Liberalism*. In this case, the rise in musical socializing in the third quarter of the nineteenth century facilitated useful bipartisan communication among statesmen and served to keep the heart supple – a priority in a period when modern progress was perceived to be so rapid as to be deleterious to the human soul. I was mostly interested in this latter book in how people lived in ways that they understood to be liberal-minded, rather than in party politics. Clubs, dinner parties and musical/literary salons nurtured bipartisan friendships, provided a tonic to overwork and were a site of soft politics. This sociability along with an attempt to better oneself through individualized study was the bedrock of a civil society. Hunnicutt's research shows how this vibrant cultural activity continued into the twentieth century alongside a decrease of work time by World War II to approximately half of what it was in the previous century (*Work* 1–2).

Simultaneously, a counterforce began to emerge with the Great Depression. The ability to work suddenly and understandably rose in importance as people were starving. According to Hunnicutt, after Franklin Delano Roosevelt, American politicians placed job creation and expansion of work at the heart of most platforms. Values fundamentally shifted from emphasizing the health of leisure time to establishing the "right to work" as a basic human right (*Kellogg's* 34).

Alongside this ideological shift, the working day, week and year continue to lengthen. Not only do most of us work longer hours today than did our parents, but economist Juliet B. Schor shares the alarming fact that by the mid-1990s the average American worked about a month more than in the 1970s (22). This movement goes in the opposite direction of "industrious capitalists like Henry Ford and AT&T's Walter Gifford," who had what amounts now to a "forgotten dream ...

that technological and social progress would lead to the gradual reduction of working hours, leaving time for worthier pursuits—." These words are found in Nathan Schneider's thoughtful consideration for *The Chronicle of Higher Education* in 2014 of Hunnicutt's work within the context of today's expectations.

Our orientation to the world needs to shift so that our ability to *be* becomes our compass. Of course, we need enough to live on, but as Hunnicutt suggests, what we require may change. The reality of long COVID reveals how vital is this reorientation. Millions of long haulers have much to contribute to workplaces, communities and families, but pacing is now essential to our ability to be productive without slipping back into ill health. Only with stopping to rest as needed will we continue to heal and have the potential fully to recover. We need to earn a living while prioritizing quality of life and well-being. Shifting cultural values so that we work to live, rather than live to work, is more urgent than ever.

ೞ৪০

When Till and I were walking yesterday on snowy Orchestra Drive, we both stopped and looked with wonder at a party of blue jays, flits of indigo overhead and on either side. The effect of scattering, moving color in the otherwise monotone landscape is breathtaking. As Emily Dickinson so aptly observed in "The Blue Jay":

> The snow and he are intimate;
> I've often seen them play
> When heaven looked upon us all
> With such severity
> I felt apology were due
> To an insulted sky,
> Whose pompous frown was nutriment
> To their temerity. (9–16)

Dickinson's consideration of the jay's playfulness during severe winter weather includes religious connotations. The heavens are the wind and snow of a harsh New England winter in the late nineteenth century; they also suggest God's judgement for lightheartedness.

While I have been thinking of the employer in the modern world and the effects of a global pandemic, this late nineteenth-century poem also expresses how we workaholics can feel the need to apologize to an overseer for taking time to play. "The Blue Jay," moreover, beautifully communicates the seeming incongruity of fun during a severe time. Elsewhere in the poem, the jay is characterized as: "Pursuing winds that

censure us / ... / The brother of the universe / Was never blown away"
(5, 7–8). Similarly: "The pillow of this daring head / Is pungent
evergreens" (17–18). Play is thus endowed with the quality of daring
and survival. It even emerges from the stern heavens: in the last two
lines of the inset quotation above, the heavenly frown feeds temerity.
The watching speaker of the poem finally considers the bird's
"character—a tonic" (21). Daring to jest during difficult times and in the
face of illness is precisely that: a tonic.

On the ground below the capering congregation of jays, a black
squirrel suddenly pursues a grey cousin. Till races forward before being
stopped by the end of his leash. Thus two playful and potentially severe
chases (the squirrels of each other, and the cat) pull me up short, too.
They interrupt my serious train of thought with the delight of
observation.

C3&O

The day before Christmas Eve is my last morning waking in the cottage.
All night, the wind and the slightly warmer temperatures caused wet
plunks of snow to fall heavily on the roof and alongside the cottage.
Cast down from neighboring trees, some plops were so loud that they
sounded like catapults thrown into our warm camp, startling cats and
myself awake from the soft doze with which we courted full slumber.

Drawing the curtains reveals a ground still snow covered, but the
trees are disburdened, their tiny branches bouncing again after several
days of stillness. They had been bowed under heavy white mantles. The
flurry of springy movement startles me, it so sharply contrasts with the
last few days of heavy, motionless boughs. Without their snowy stripes,
I recognize the emergent trees as my warm weather companions. The
prospect from the window thus marries the calm of the winter snow-
covered ground with the blurred vista of russet, grey and green that
extended through the forest, and which I had admired all autumn.
Viewed thus, the world comprises two seasons; the simultaneity inspires
me to think that it is possible to have an inner bearing that coexists with
the external world, to mutual advantage.

Similarly, when I drove to my parents' house last night, I spied a
mid-sized beech with most of its yellow leaves still attached, standing
against a taller grove of bare trees. From a distance in the late afternoon
glow, it looked like a pale gold triangle on a field of white, against a
silvery filigree forest. These shoulder seasons combine to create
unexpected splendor just off the well-travelled roads.

Yesterday morning, deer tracks revealed that several of our peaceful friends had wended their way that morning up to the cottage and back again to the conservancy. Here were hooves walking down our road, turning at Orchestra Drive. Then three sets of tracks raced down the hill toward the swamp while one made its way sedately down the snowy road to the lake stairs. Turning here, it descended the treads, crossed the boardwalk, traversed the path to the lake and then returned partway before disappearing into the bracken of the now-frozen bog.

We see a lot of avian activity and busy squirrels at present, but the world otherwise quieted when the snow came to stay. These deer tracks along my usual ways are a reminder of the wildlife that walks among us, even when so many hibernating creatures are sleeping all around.

Now, I prepare to leave the cottage because of the forecast: rain turning to snow with a projected eight to ten inches of accumulation. The roads will ice under a thick weight of winter white. It will look glorious, but also prove impassible for me in my small red bug. The paved roads on which the arrow tree sits are plowed infrequently and the dirt roads of the colony not at all. At a certain point around Christmas, the snow will settle in to stay until March. I do not want to become stuck here, unable to get the car out.

So I wake this morning, trying to savor the quiet as the curtains gradually lighten with dawn and the skylight shows the white sky with bare branches swinging rhythmically back and forth, like the sweep of an inverted broom across the heavens. Needles of the white pine in front remain curiously still; the whole bough moves, not the individual green tines.

There is much in me that would just stay here if I could, but I have begun to linger longer each evening after dinner with my family. Even while orienting more toward the exterior world, I simultaneously have the quiet of the last few months stored up. Wordsworth reminds us in "Tintern Abbey" that recollections are there to be tapped into. As well as a memory, tranquility is a way of being and the deepest core of self. The last two are really the same.

So the boughs sway, not as a good-bye wave, but rather as a reminder of how to hold fast to this way of being. When the wind buffets the forest, the tree remains elastic, moving agreeably rather than breaking. All the while, this leafy being remains calm, offering aid to others through its sheltering branches and its medicinal aroma, communicating with the larger community through its interlocking roots while simultaneously reaching for the sky.

It reminds me of my walk a couple weeks ago when I suddenly found the eagles' nest. It was breathtaking! I was travelling along a stretch of path that I hadn't previously visited and happened to look up.

There it was, unmistakable. The nest was at least six feet in diameter if not more, a circle formed by large grey sticks with the bark worn off, crisscrossed like Lincoln Logs at odd latticework angles. It would have been difficult for me to lift many of these fairly large tree limbs.

Encountering an eagle aerie is so unusual that it does not seem to be a part of any usual symbolic belief, although the birds themselves are sacred warriors and healers to the local Odawa people. It is rare to find the nest of these noble birds. In 1978, bald eagles were placed on the endangered list. Luckily their population has been increasing and they are now a protected species. The location of their nests is a zealously guarded secret by park rangers, for disturbing the area scares off the eagles.

When I mentioned my experience to Mike Chamberlain, IAA's retired ecology teacher, he suggested that if the pair had successfully mated, then a brown bird should be in the area. I could be on the look out.

Mike's comment caused me to reflect on my eagle journey during recent weeks, from Chipmunk's warning, to seeing a juvenile eagle, witnessing a pair of bald eagles launching from their piney perch, and now finding a nest. Sometimes, the wild does seem to offer a personal message. The young eagle had been the first of an amazing set of sightings that revealed themselves one right after another and then came full circle again when Mike mentioned that I might actively look for the juvenile.

Put another way, the avian adult life cycle begins with the flight of birds away from a nest. In acupuncture terms, this feathered journey is understood as similar to the element of metal. If the metal remains unbalanced with other elements, then the bird will never return. The elements need each other. A holistic body experiences a release and a return, like the eagles' journey that begins and ends in a nest made of earthy mud and sticks. Symbolically, it matches my own path away from my Michigan home into the professional world, and then back to the cottage in the woods for a healing journey. Thought of in terms of my transatlantic sense of self, it also recalls my travel in metal airplanes back and forth across the ocean, only to find myself grounded for a time in my own childhood nest here, near the arrow tree. Like the early inhabitants of this land who journeyed between winter homeland to the summer village of Waganakising, the trail markers serve as guideposts for safely traversing land and water routes; heading out and back again in cyclical motion.

Discovering the aerie seemed the last in a precisely unfolding narrative. As the home of the visionary eagles who carry illness to be healed, the nest seemed a confirmation that my self is found through my connection with intuitions. Furthermore, I could believe my acupuncturists and my medical doctor when they agreed that I did not present like someone who would have a lifetime of chronic illness. I am returning to work with the goal of integrating professional skills with the original joy and balance of my earlier years.

HREE nights at my parents' comfortable house resulted in three mornings when I awoke feeling completely wrecked inside. Having gone to sleep exhausted with foggy COVID headaches each night, I slept deeply and awoke shattered, as if my nervous system had been run over in the night and walked the next day like living road kill. Put another way, it felt like fingernails scratching relentlessly, ceaselessly, on an interior chalkboard. Of course, I loved being present for the holiday with its gingerbread houses, carols, tree trimming, sledding, snowmen, Christmas cookies, joyful gift-giving, and celebratory feast with partner, child and parents. I'm so glad to have been there for the glow of family. That said, I did experience a setback.

Once again, I made the decision to head for the woods.

Returning to the cottage two days ago, I discovered a community of animal tracks. Here were three deer grouped together and one slightly apart, crossing the snow-covered dirt turning to the cottage. The toes of each hoof print narrowed and almost closed, forming a sort of arrow pointing in the direction of travel. Interspersed with these deer prints were squirrel paws playfully crisscrossing: now springing far apart in leaps and then appearing closer to each other in little scampers and hops. These tracks even ran across the fresh snow right in front of the cottage, frolicking up to the doorstep, the base of overhanging hemlock and back again, a complex dance moves diagram on the forest floor. The snow thus marks not only the passing of an unseen creature, but also reveals part of its character through these gamboling pirouettes and pivots. I had mistakenly thought that my woodland home stood quiet for the three days of Christmas when I stayed with Mom and Dad along with Bruce and Hollis. In fact, the deer and squirrels left evidence of joyful and peaceful presences surrounding the little cabin in the woods.

These paw prints in the snow have points in common with beliefs about the shadow as articulated by Chief Stephen Augustine, a tribal elder of the Elsipogtog First Nation in New Brunswick. He passes on the oral tradition of his people in "Mi'kmaq Creation Story": "When we stand in the Sun we cast a shadow. The shadow represents the spirits of our ancestors. Grandfather Sun puts spirit into life" (27). The Wabanaki nations of northern Maine also think of the shadow as an essential part of a human being, whereby the ancestors are co-present with the living person. The traces in the snow similarly remind us that whole beings have passed this way: more than inanimate physical remnants, tracks are impressions made by lively spirits.

Both shadows and snow prints thus reveal beings that are and are not here. It requires no expertise in tracking to find creaturely evidence in recent snow, just as shadow-seeking is possible in most lights, if only you focus your attention.

A poem from the Song period in China makes a similar comparison between our lives and an animal's footprints in winter. As translated into English, it refers either to a wild swan or a snow goose:

> To what should we compare human life? It should
> be compared to a wild goose trampling on the snow.
> The snow retains for a moment the imprint of its feet;
> the goose flies away no one know where.
>
> Su Dungpo, trans. Simon Leys

Simply paraphrased, a human being briefly walks on the earth before his or her soul flies away into the unknown. More complexly, the earth marks the presence of the bird as a momentary impression before two types of ephemera occur: flight (without footprints) and the melting of snow. The oneness of the living being and the earth is also implied by the shared whiteness of the graceful bird and the snowy earth.

The poem's treatment of swans reminds me of my last acupuncture session. Two swans had been swimming all day on the Boardman River outside the window. It was unusual for swans to be on that section of the water, let alone to remain for so long. Abigail pointed out the snowy pair to me as she came into the room and noticed that a female Mallard duck had temporarily joined them.

After my treatment, Abigail looked out the window and saw that they had all flown away during my healing session. "Perhaps they were waiting for you," she commented. "What do you make of that?" In an interconnected world, people and animals are understood to tap into each other's energetic signatures, although we humans have differing levels of sensitivity and awareness.

That day, the swans reminded me of the many times that my mother would take my brother and me to Logan's Landing where the river empties into Boardman Lake. The swans normally hang out there. It always seemed magical to see flocks of swans, Canada geese and various types of ducks swimming in water that remained unfrozen all winter. Breaking off from the rest of the bevy, the couplet of swans seemed to be offering a friendly greeting at acupuncture. I failed to see any additional significance that day.

Upon reflection, however, the poem from China's eleventh century reminds me that majestic swans have been present in my life from childhood, faithful to each other and to me. They would, for example, wander up on the bank of our house on Duck Lake in the summer. At acupuncture, the waterfowl seemed to wait for me before flying away "no one knows where," like the snowy footprints of deer and squirrel that reveal that they had passed this way. These animals leave their imprint on my life. Disclosing the character of their path (together, alone; jumping, standing, dancing) is strangely intimate: a window into their life journeys after they are no longer physically present, which in turn I absorb into my own path as I reflect upon them. They thus leave impressions upon me.

It reverses the children's game, "Fox and Geese," which we played in Michigan winters. On the playground at school, we would stamp out a circle with two or three prongs running to the center, an assigned "safe" space. It resembled a peace sign with a reprieve from the chase at its heart. The designated fox would pursue the other children (geese) around the path, attempting with a touch to transform the tagged child into the new fox. We followed the snowy paths, mostly didn't stray from the trodden way, our footsteps packing the snow harder as we inhabited the character of animals and freely metamorphosized back and forth: now goose, now fox. Like the poem, our human lives were directly compared to the snow goose: the tracks our own as we playfully channeled the chase of wild animals. This game must surely have originated from tracks seen in the pristine winter world.

ॐ

In the quiet of the cottage, I experienced deep, restorative slumber again. It took three days to return to a semblance of where I had previously been in my healing.

I could connect with the peaceful world found in the snow, but it was clear that I was easily overwhelmed by a normal household: simultaneous conversational exchanges, music, television, bleeps and buzzes, loud footsteps on the floor overhead, and frequent interruptions when people spoke. The restorative calm of the woods, in contrast, mirrored the inner peace of a healthy *shen* of the spirit. I was building myself up again, constructing myself anew, beginning with the inner core and nurtured by the serenity of wild energies. Being in normal, civilized life was just too much. I wasn't strong enough yet. This realization startled me, for it implies that we spend a lot of energy in filtering through the sensory load of modern life. When we have our health and are neurotypical, we don't necessarily realize how tiring this ongoing bustle can be.

Before I worked this out, I sank into a two-day depression caused by the implications of not being strong enough to return to daily life with my family. Would I ever get well enough to resume my normal activities, including my job? Would I be able to do so in a time frame that didn't cause us serious financial problems? Logically, I knew that I was getting better. Looking back at Chapter 9 reminded me of the tiredness that had accompanied my previous attempt to move to Mom and Dad's. That sleep had been even worse. Comparing past and present offered reassurance and clarity about what was happening now, ten weeks later.

I am obviously recovering, but my healing will go faster if I don't overthink or worry about how long it will take. The best thing is to be back at the cottage where I can tap into the healing energies of the natural world with its negative ions, peaceful atmosphere and aerosol of positive forest bacteria. All of these things support a constitutional regularity that works with the deep sleep, joy and beauty of the wild. Rather than fret about uncertainties (when exactly will I get well?), my focus needs to be on helpful certainties, like the healing that occurs in flourishing ecosystems.

I look down again at the paw and hoof traces in the snow. Here are paths through the woods. To me, the wild signifies more than a place apart from urban life. The idea of human ecology includes not only the synergistic existence with nature, but also the ability to exist peacefully with uncertainties through finding an inner stillness. The arrow-shaped hoof prints thus seem to make a more improvisational path than do the frequented trails marked by bent arrow trees. This "not knowing" state reminds me to just sit with it; to be, and not to worry about the doing.

I make a path in the snow, too. My booted feet had clearly trekked to Polly's house and this led our neighbor, Ericka, to ask today if I would like for her to clear a path for me. She loves to create sweet little walkways, from decorative garden paths made by weaving together fallen branches to shoveling snow. In the same conversation, Ericka asked if I had been out on my cross-country skis earlier. Skis leave fascinating tracks because the skier's size and direction can be difficult to ascertain. My tracks originated and ended at my front step, but an observer needed to stand near the cottage to know this. I, too, have left information in the snow, which led Ericka correctly to surmise and show interest in my activities and intents.

It turns out that we had both been reading the animal tracks down by the lake. Coyote, we had each concluded. I had looked up the differences between coyote and dog prints the previous day (coyote paws are more oval and have pronounced claws at the toes). Crows had left Y's in the snow. I saw that deer ventured onto the ice forming at the shore. Undoubtedly, the wildlife take note of my boot prints after I have passed, too. This crisscross of informational exchange feels strangely intimate and vulnerable. Perhaps the latter feeling is a primal remnant, for tracking is obviously also used in hunting.

In contrast, our attention to each other is simply curious. It highlights how the world's beings take mutual interest in each other's traces, attempting to know through them. This investigation includes the physical prints and, more searchingly, the intent with which they were made.

Making tracks is not unlike my own writing. Dark ink fills up the ivory paper as I first handwrote these journals. Writing is central to my recovery process because it helps me to evolve understandings about what makes a life worth living. The mind leads the way and then traditional Eastern medicine offers physical support for that processing. As I looked again at this writing and decided to revise it, my lessons deepened in the process of entering it into the laptop and seeing black footprints emerge now as letters, words and paragraphs gradually filling the white screen. The word processing screen lengthens as I progress down my own written path. Now, I am not only making marks for myself, but also for anyone who wants to follow, like printing in the snow.

Thought of in another way, this writing process is not unlike the arrow tree. "If you are lucky enough to run into a crooked tree, know that it didn't happen by accident," Eric Hemenway counsels. "Protect them, revere them, know their significance" (Driscoll). I might add: pass on the story that they tell of human beings navigating in synergy with the earth.

☙❧

Light playing on the snow in morning creates dark shades and white paths of sunlight, like little dunes. Some mornings, the wind has smoothed the snow into a seemingly uniform surface, but not today. I cannot help but view the world in *yin-yang* terms now.

The mounding of the ground reminds me of the practical need to make arrangements about where to park my car. Ericka and Andy, my closest neighbors, live right off the paved road which the county plows. My friends have agreed that I can park there beginning tonight, when another winter system is expected. I'll have to walk back to the cottage. It isn't far, but it will become more difficult as the snow deepens, especially if I am carrying a load. It will be helpful to keep the path well-trodden on a daily basis.

Icicles drip from the eaves, creating lines that shimmer before the equally straight dark lines of the trees. It's like looking out from the maw of a creature, as if the cottage has yawned, hunched and dreamy in the winter landscape. Echoing this personification, I draw up the covers, hunker down, and sleep.

ᑳᔒ

The new year rings in with joyful welcome worldwide. We are all ready to be done with 2020, undeniably an *annus horribilis*. It reminds me of Tennyson's great elegiac poem, *In Memoriam A.H.H.*, where the turning years are marked with church bells ringing. Canto 106 begins:

> Ring out, wild bells, to the wild sky,
>> The flying cloud, the frosty light:
>> The year is dying in the night;
> Ring out, wild bells, and let him die. (1–4)

I share the sense of wild celebration, where the clouds scurry-sweep the old year out under a frosty, clear night of hope.

Normally, I write in my journal on New Year's Eve, reflecting on what has been and what might be. I have no need of this on December 31, 2020, for *The Arrow Tree* is my comprehensive reflection. "Ring out old shapes of foul disease," I echo with Tennyson and then say a hearty Amen to the final stanza: "Ring in the valiant man and free, / The larger heart, the kindlier hand; / Ring out the darkness of the land" (25, 29–31). With this prayer, the "frosty light" of the new year emerges.

We share Tennyson's sentiment here in snowy Michigan, although our new year is quiet with silver frost and deer tracks that reveal soulful presences moving silently through the juniper green all around us. Each set of tracks weaves peaceful energy like multi-dimensional strands in life's tapestry, extending up from the footprint to the lingering imprint of the deer's warm body, shimmering like a shadowy presence. These energetic traces of graceful steps guided by sensitive ears and deep pools of eyes are warm like a spirit blanket in the silence of a snowy midnight, gleaming white under a clear northern sky.

This sky remains a guide for the tracks in our lives, too. When I was a student at Cambridge, I remember the disorientation when I looked up one night from King's Parade where I stood next to the Church of St. Mary the Great. To my confusion, it appeared as if the big dipper was turned upside down. Since then, I've learned that time of night as well as seasonal shifts could account for the appearance. At that moment, however, the immensity hit me of how far away I was from Michigan.

Having now called England home for much of my adult life, I no longer feel perplexed when I look up to find Polaris. Its simple presence pointing north is a comfort, no matter whether the latitude makes it appear higher or lower. I like to think of my friends and family around the world similarly tilting their chins, gazing at the night sky, searching for the north star. In so doing, we look away from cell phones to contemplate the heavens and our place in the universe. It's humbling. We could all use that search for perspective in the "wild sky," finding there Grandmother Moon reminding us of the continuing presence and guidance of our natural origins.

Three days later, as the tires of my little red VW bug made tracks to my parents' home, I saw a pair of wild turkeys waiting by the roadside. They stood stolidly as I approached, drew alongside and passed. One was near the roadside looking at me and the other was just off the bank, gazing into the woods. I'm reminded of the Anishinaabe elder Simon Otto's insight that birds are hit by cars because they are used to flying in forests; since moving machinery is not part of their lives, they are confused and scared when they encounter cars (66). Somehow, these turkeys had become familiar enough with the human world to stand still when cars zipped by. Moreover, the direction of their eyes (one pair toward me and the other toward the forest) perfectly mirrored the directions of my own contemplation.

Wild turkeys are ungainly birds, seemingly rooted to the earth, but also capable of flight. Seeing the turkeys in winter made the flying turkeys from our spring hike seem prescient. If you'll recall, Hollis and I saw a small flock take wing the day before we fell ill. My experience with COVID-19 was therefore bookended by wild turkeys, from the live virus to now as I near the end of full-time convalescence.

Turkeys used to be prevalent in the woodlands around the Great Lakes and were part of Anishinaabek feasts and celebrations (Rempel 75, 84; Duric). They were emblems of abundance through sacrifice. Only now as I see the wild turkeys for a second time does their original flight through the woods and into the sky seem a foreshadowing of what was about to happen. For I, too, characterize my struggle with the novel coronavirus as a sacrifice leading to unexpected blessings.

C≥Ǝ৪৩

I'm so pleased to be about to change my label from "Survived: Recovering" to partial remission, or what I'm thinking of as "Survived: Rebalancing." Hip, Hip, Hooray!! For long haulers, each success story offers hope to the larger community. I will certainly miss waking to snowy Michigan mornings, but I'm thankful to be feeling well enough to return to St. Louis and to teach my delayed graduate class (through video and audio conferencing technology). I'm still easily tired, but that's normal after any major illness. My acupuncturist has validated my own instinct that it will probably take me another year until I have fully regained strength. She held her hand about four feet off the ground to show my usual baseline of health and then described my current functioning at about a foot below that.

Amidst many cautions to pace myself, I have wondered practically how to balance the demands of workplace and homeschooling with the necessary rest. What happens next?

The answer, I believe, is like the fluid motion of kayaking, where one arm pushes while the other pulls the paddle, and then they switch and the pushing arm pulls while the other pushes. As Chapter 11 discussed, there are always endangering situations and people to guard against (push them away), but luckily there are also many aspects of my work environment to welcome (pull in the positive energy). I can decide to help my pericardium – that watchdog of the *shen* of the heart and the spirit – rather than feel afraid that I will not be able to manage reentry. In actual fact, I have all the resources that I need.

Practically speaking, my ongoing strategy for full recovery begins with reassessing what I deem to be a normal workload. What I had perceived as the norm – twelve-hour workdays plus weekends – is stressful, excessive and unsustainable. I need to recalibrate so that my expectations are realistic and closer to forty-hour workweeks. Regular acupuncture and taking naps will also be crucial for the time being, for many long haulers are reporting a cycle of relapses without warning. The point is not to deplete energy, but rather to continue to build it, no matter how gradually.

New beginnings offer opportunities. They always do. The next phase in life can be about becoming better, in all senses. I actually have no choice but to learn how to form new, more holistic habits or I will slip back into illness.

There is a circularity and movement forward in this process. As the first-ever National Youth Poet Laureate Amanda Gorman articulated in a stunning piece of performance poetry for the 2021 presidential inauguration:

> For while we have our eyes on the future,
> History has its eyes on us (56–7).

These two lines contribute to the conceptual circularity of "The Hill We Climb," a poem that plays with how words and ideas first relate through sound and then change:

So while once we asked: How could we possibly prevail over
  catastrophe?
Now we assert: How could catastrophe possibly prevail over us?

We will not march back to what was,
But move to what shall be:
A country that is bruised but whole,
Benevolent but bold,
Fierce and free. (65–71)

We could easily substitute "A long hauler" for "A country." Gorman's
words speak truths that she did not necessarily intend, but which have
nevertheless helped me to imagine how to take the next step forward
into the future, "bruised but whole, / Benevolent but bold, / Fierce and
free," like the enduring arrow tree.

The power of the creative word to heal and to ignite us deserves to
be celebrated along with the sentiments of Gorman's poem. The poem
"stole the show" as *The Guardian* observed from across the Atlantic
(Gorman). If we look back on American history to Robert Frost's
"Dedication," the first poem to be written for a presidential
inauguration (John F. Kennedy's in 1961), we see a reminder of the
importance of wordsmiths: "Summoning artists to participate / In the
august occasions of the state / Seems something for us all to celebrate"
(1–3). Indeed. Creative thinking-through-writing has been the most
important ingredient to my "prevail[ing] over catastrophe," aiding my
healing and, I hope, that of others, too.

I am ready to send sickness away like a cumbersome turkey taking
wing. It makes me happy to be returning to the classroom where I can
teach about the profound importance of creativity to the human spirit.
I look forward to returning to my destiny by way of beginnings,
navigating the path indicated by the dear oak arrow tree.

Appendix A | Our Long COVID

> survivor relief
> one year — anger and grief. Long
> covidersary

found myself writing this haiku at the first anniversary of becoming ill from COVID-19 – the "covidersary." At that point, I experienced a strong emotional cocktail that, frankly, took me by surprise. While *The Arrow Tree* focuses on a process of healing during the second five months of illness, it may be useful to contextualize this period with the before and after details, from the onset of symptoms through to the year anniversary, vaccination and beyond. In so doing, I can set the stage with a clear onset point and I can say that my story has been one of mostly increasing physical health, but the conclusion is a little blurry.

No matter how much any of us desire it to be otherwise, long COVID is currently an open-ended story for most individual cases, the epidemic itself and the social impact. I have in mind Felicity Callard's prescient observation that long COVID does not have the sort of plotline that Charles E. Rosenberg posits in his influential article of 1989, "What Is an Epidemic." Rosenberg argues that epidemics, as a social phenomenon, "start at a moment in time, proceed on a stage limited in space and duration, follow a plot line of increasing and revelatory tension, move to a crisis of individual and collective character, then drift toward closure" (2). Callard counters this dramaturgy in the Winter 2020 issue of the *Bulletin of the History of Medicine;* she theorizes that the end is not clear when viewed from the perspective of the sickbed. "Such a horizontal body," Callard writes, "is in a cognitively and affectively different place from that inhabited by vertical others" (728). For long haulers, COVID is simply "long!" – much longer than the two weeks that was originally assigned to CV-19 (Callard 738).

Time thus operates indistinctly within long experiences of COVID-19. It doesn't progress linearly, as medical terminology implies when "speaking in terms of the chronic, the progressive, and the terminal, of relapses and stages." These last are Ellen Samuels's words in a creative nonfiction essay in which she considers "crip time," or the embodiment of time and energy experienced by some disabled individuals.

Diagnostic language essentially denies the reality of crip time as a sort of "*time travel* ... of backward and forward acceleration, jerky stops and starts, tedious intervals and abrupt endings" (Samuels; original emphasis). Words like "post," conversely, offer reassurance, as in Chronic Post-COVID Syndrome. Such vocabulary seems authoritative because it originates with physicians. It therefore influences popular perceptions and attitudes, often to the detriment of the suffering person. In the question-and-answer session after her keynote address for the UK's Northern Network for Medical Humanities Research Congress 2021, Callard summed up the very real consequences when "long" is understood by the larger culture to stop after a period of time, such as a year: "violence is attached to denial of ongoing disabilities."

In contrast, I found it helpful when a friend introduced me to "The Spoon Theory," a short piece of lifewriting by Christine Miserandino that has become a conceptual aid within the chronic illness community for understanding energy resources. In the essay, Miserandino imagines each exertion by an individual as a unit of a spoon. Unlike the non-disabled person who seems to have an endless supply of spoons, a "spoonie" has a finite number each day (say, twelve spoons). Therefore, activities need to be thought through in advance, because when the spoons are spent, the day's supply is exhausted. Thus if on top of daily caretaking (a spoon each for getting up and making a meal), I engage in a high-energy activity like teaching (maybe six spoons), then I cannot also have a twenty-minute walk that day or a Zoom meeting without tipping into post-exertional malaise. Some reserves of energy and time need to be in place, too, for attending to surprises like our son's relapses and for my own daily selfcare, which may consume or replenish spoons. As Samuels beautifully recognizes, crip time is about "*time travel*" and "*broken time*," and it is also about "*grief time*" and "*writing time*" (original emphasis). For me, such writing has been essential for maintaining and deepening inner peace and acceptance.

I'll begin by narrating how seriously ill we were between March 26th and early July 2020. Besides my own illness during this time, Bruce and I had to advocate repeatedly for our young son with an unresponsive health care system that either refused to run any of the most common tests or did so begrudgingly after repeated requests. Many people both inside and outside the halls of medicine disbelieved what we were experiencing because our symptoms did not fit how the world first understood the disease and because we did not have a positive test among us, as I'll explain below. We did, however, have the travel history and a set of symptoms that did not fit any other diagnosis.

After surviving the virus, my ongoing symptoms and blood work led my doctor strongly to advise full rest. By the end of a five-month medical leave, I was feeling well enough to return to work. I still had some elevated numbers, but was nevertheless deemed sufficiently recovered to resume working life in late January 2021. A couple months later, I found that I needed to address a complex set of emotions at becoming so very ill in the first place. For me, mourning, rage and frustration emerged when I was no longer at risk of being controlled by these feelings; I could address them without tipping over into illness.

Besides being stronger, my sense that it's safe now to confront difficult feelings comes from being lucky enough to be situated in a mostly sympathetic community. In this situation, anger at what has happened to me has felt like a mobilizing emotion. Many other first wavers, however, have experienced disbelief and even abandonment by friends and family. Feelings of disassociation and deep depression are terrible in themselves. They can also lead to additional disorders.

The American Psychological Association (APA) already finds that a second pandemic, this time of mental health, is upon us. A national survey conducted by the Harris Poll for the APA in February 2021 indicated that "physical health may be declining due to an inability to cope in healthy ways" including significant weight changes, increased alcohol consumption and sleep deprivation. "These reported health impacts signal many adults may be having difficulties managing stressors, including grief and trauma, and are likely to lead to significant, long-term individual and societal consequences, including chronic illness." It's sobering to realize how the linked health of minds, bodies and spirits is at issue for individuals and wider communities. The poll results also indicate the groups of people who experience the greatest stress ("parents, essential workers, young people and people of color"). It is unclear how the survey was organized, but it may be fair to assume that it did not ask long haulers to self-identify. I suspect that if it had, then long haulers would have topped the list alongside the others in the citation.

Surviving

On Thursday, March 12, 2020, the first case of the novel coronavirus was reported in Cambridge, England, where I had been on sabbatical. I found out the same day upon landing in Chicago O'Hare when a friend from Cambridgeshire texted to tell me. We both wondered if I had left just in time. On the fourteenth day after my arrival back in the USA (a time of quarantine for our family), however, we all fell ill. My husband, Bruce, had COVID relatively lightly. His terrible fatigue lasted four days and then he was on his feet and working normally again. Hollis (then nine years old) and I became very ill.

For just over three months, our son and I had continuous run-over-by-a-truck fatigue, he had painful gastrointestinal issues, and we both had other symptoms that waxed and waned. We had variously among us and at different points for the next three months: muscle ache, a broken bone, debilitating headache, fever, hot flashes, tingly feeling in the lower lungs, intermittent dry cough, sore throat, loss of appetite, itchy rashes, nausea, dizziness, tingly hands and feet, tingly top of the head, scratchy eyes, dips in oxygen level, increased pulse, and shortness of breath and tiredness after small amounts of exercise.

Despite keeping a journal since I was fourteen, there are weeks of blank spaces from late March until the end of June. I was too ill to write much, except for an occasional entry, such as: "I've never been so ill before. It's *terrible* to feel so weak." For weeks, we made progress at the rate of two steps forward and one or two back.

Writing from the frontlines of CV-19 mostly occurred during these spring months in a series of Facebook posts to a closed group of friends. Because Hollis and I became so ill and in such unexpected ways, I decided to share our experience in case it helped others to spot the symptoms that were not yet associated with COVID-19. So many aspects of this coronavirus were underreported or misrepresented, including what children experienced. In the harrowing month of May, for example, I found myself communicating:

> Day 53: We're off to the ER again. Hollis's fever up to 39.9 C this morning (104 F), high pulse, extreme headache, losing sense of smell, muscle aches, and worrying fever deliriums last night. That's a very high fever for a child.
>
> We were ignored early on because we didn't have extreme fever and trouble breathing, but our symptoms match those now recognized by leading scientists. We've been talking with doctors locally, and with medical professional friends in the US and in the UK, and we've been reading their recommended articles.
>
> Day 55: Thank you for wanting to know how we're doing. I've waited to post our update until I was in a more positive place. We came home late on Sunday from the ER, with H's fever down. He has only had liquids (including broth), rice, porridge and applesauce for four days now because of terrible stomach pain. We're still having to rely upon our own home cures. I continue to battle illness myself.
>
> It's a toss-up as to whether we'll get a medical doctor who cites the test like gospel and treats us pejoratively, suggesting that we just

have a bad flu (trust me – this thing isn't anything like a flu!), or a medical doctor who says, "Of course you have COVID – everything fits, and I recognize your symptoms."

Postings such as these were to prove invaluable as our illness dragged on because I was able to construct a timeline for our doctors of the progression of the disease.

Among our friends, I found a grateful audience and was contacted privately by those whose family members had similar symptoms. People of all ages were searching for explanations, support and community in a period when our experiences were not commonly recognized. Friends articulated that they were grateful to hear our cautionary tale since they knew of no one else who was infected. My Facebook posts reminded them to be vigilant in their personal safety, especially after enduring months of social isolation. In spring 2021, they began to report that they used our example with friends who felt that vitamins were all the protection needed against CV-19; as a result of hearing about us, a few more people were vaccinated. Receiving this sort of positive feedback reciprocally supported me in my own struggles. There's synergy as we help each other. It took being willing to open up and share to start that process. As a result, this extended community asked how I was doing, believed in me and offered practical assistance. As it turned out, this support was extremely lucky; I learned later that many long haulers not only endure the disbelief of their closest family and friends, but also sometimes find themselves abandoned when they most need love, encouragement, affirmation and concrete assistance.

Because the medical establishment could offer no assistance to us while we were suffering other than the advice to seek emergency help if we had trouble breathing, we had to rely on our own resources. I'm not a medical doctor, and those who are feeling poorly should definitely consult with a physician, but sharing what was helpful has become part of the story of long COVID, within my own network and the larger global community as found in social media groups run by and for long haulers. There is a generosity of spirit among those who have fallen ill.

In our journey, rest and staying well hydrated were important. Acupuncture proved especially helpful in treating our symptoms, along with Nambudripad's Allergy Elimination Techniques (NAET). Like many within the long-haul community, we also found some supplements to be particularly useful. I still take Omega-CoQ10 and Vitamins D, C and a multi-B. More recently, I added a probiotic. Others find zinc to be helpful. COVID is an inflammatory disease, so our household follows a diet rich in leafy greens, hibiscus tea and a dairy-free turmeric tea made with black pepper and coconut oil (the interaction of ingredients makes it effective).

In the middle of June 2020, the Infectious Diseases unit at our local university research hospital confirmed that we had entered the post-viral (non-infectious) phase. We continued to suffer fatigue and other symptoms, although thankfully our son's continuous gastrointestinal issues had finally disappeared. During July and August, Hollis's other symptoms went away and he gathered strength. By autumn, he appeared fully recovered, although he would suffer a relapse as January turned to February 2021.

For me, the summer comprised attempts to work remotely while still battling considerable ill health. It was only as Hollis finally began to improve that I had the space to turn my attention to myself and to have blood work ordered. The results revealed alarmingly high liver enzymes such as are consistent with viral infection. At the end of August 2020, I followed medical advice to take a leave from work in order to rest and get better. Around this time, I also began to have floaters in my eye and discovered a tear in the retina, which occasioned multiple visits to the ophthalmologist and a retina specialist, but finally seemed to resolve itself. This alarming situation with my sight may have been an unfortunate coincidence, or not.

Exactly five months after first falling ill, I shared with my Facebook friends that I'd taken a semester's leave. The post conveys the state of my health and my approach to recovery:

> I want to highlight the after-effects of this illness, which are ongoing for millions of people, impacting both quality of life and productivity. For myself, among other challenges, I have continuing extreme nausea, weakness and fatigue. I also experienced vertigo for the first time a fortnight ago.
>
> My posts and photos reflect the beauty, positive thinking, creativity and loving community that aid recovery, but they do not often overtly say that I am indeed in a recovery period. Yet the two are linked. The recovery is long and it is my daily reality, but so, too, is the strength that I find in these northern woods and waters. And, really, I want to focus on things of beauty and to share joy.

The Arrow Tree proper communicates the shape that my recovery took from August 2020 through January 2021, focusing on the journey to health along the lines mentioned above.

Survived: Recovering

For the second five months after becoming ill, I referred to myself as "Survived: Recovering." This long-haul phase included continuing headache, nausea, dizziness, fatigue, exercise intolerance and sleep disturbance. I was experiencing these symptoms in the first five months, too, before they were understood as consistent with the novel coronavirus. By summer, however, they were all recognized symptoms.

Living with long COVID is the current reality of millions of people worldwide. The condition is now recognized by the World Health Organization (WHO), the United States Centers for Disease Control and Prevention (CDC), National Health Service (NHS) England and leading peer-reviewed medical journals like *The Lancet.* "Multiorgan symptoms after COVID-19," the last reported on December 12, 2020, "range from cough and shortness of breath, to fatigue, headache, palpitations, chest pain, joint pain, physical limitations, depression, and insomnia, and affect people of varying ages." In advance of publishing the peer-reviewed article, *The Lancet* presented an editorial about Bin Cao's research on the "dysfunctions and complications" that persisted in patients for six months or more. The most common symptoms after six months are fatigue, post-exertional malaise and cognitive dysfunction ("Facing Up to Long COVID"; Davis).

Long haulers are frequently rendered invisible to those members of the medical profession who only respond to positive SARS-CoV-2 tests (either diagnostic or antibody). Thankfully, on December 18, 2020, the National Institute for Health and Care Excellence in Britain (NICE) published a guideline for diagnosing long COVID based on "signs and symptoms that develop during or after an infection consistent with COVID-19, continue for more than 12 weeks and are not explained by an alternative diagnosis." For whatever reason, approximately three-quarters of long haulers seem to test negative when they do have access to a test (Davis). Yet there is no doubt that as of January 2021, approximately seven million people globally have debilitating, chronic conditions, and the numbers are growing. According to *The Lancet,* the dismissal of cases by medical professionals poses dangerous risks to patients, as evinced in "slowly evolving knowledge of other poorly understood conditions (such as chronic pain and functional disorders)." What to do about the seriousness of long COVID was debated in the UK House of Commons on January 14, 2021 when multiple Members of Parliament argued that diagnosis by symptoms was the best practice for long COVID and, furthermore, that this condition exists in children.

My health profile and travel history led my doctor to diagnose me with COVID-19. I am grateful to be visible in this way, for I do not have a positive SARS-CoV-2 test. While my physician was willing to order an antibody test, I followed his counsel not to take it because of testing inaccuracies and the potential problems that ensue when negative tests become a part of patient records (see James D. Walsh). In these cases, many doctors will not look past the negative test on file to assess a person's fuller health profile.

As seen in the preceding pages, my path to increasing physical wellness during my medical leave concentrated on finding a spiritual health that was intrinsically connected to the land itself. It also included the rest prescribed by my doctor.

Survived: Rebalancing

Now, I have joined the small percentage of those long haulers who seem to have physically recovered, mostly. I returned to my university job at the end of January 2021, or five months after my medical leave began and ten months after falling ill. Teaching and other job duties were once again possible, but I tired easily. If I overworked, a post-exertional malaise set in for the remainder of the day. I had never been so ill before and, while my overall trajectory continues to be one of gradual improvement, I am still weak compared to my pre-coronavirus health. Luckily, I have a good working environment and am able to communicate openly with my line managers. Bringing other colleagues up to date is more patchy, however; since we are not yet working in person, they can neither observe my physical bearing nor can we catch up over the proverbial water cooler.

When I returned to work, I began to think of myself as "Survived: Rebalancing," a stage that I conceived as somewhat like partial remission to cancer survivors when most signs of a disease and its symptoms are gone, but not all. On the simplest level, my aim during "rebalancing" is to get to the end of the day without having reached a tipping point; such an approach allows me to reenter working life while also rebuilding health. I have also found some replenishing pursuits: forest bathing, napping, singing, creative writing and t'ai chi. For me, each day needs to include a couple of these health-giving activities because they will help to increase energetic reserves over time. They also help me to maintain that calm center that aligns with holistic health.

Although there is much that we don't know about long COVID, it is known that recovery from a major illness – any major illness – can take a couple years. With a disease like long CV-19 that ebbs and flows, relapses can and do occur, as reported by other long haulers who also became ill before April 2020. Our ten-year-old son, who appeared to make a full recovery in summer 2020, relapsed at the end of January 2021. Six weeks later, his symptoms had largely eased up after weekly acupuncture, rest and supplements. He was even almost out of the foot brace from when he fractured his toe (he stubbed it in the house; bone issues are consistent with long COVID). At three months, however, his extreme fatigue is only worsening. Stomach pain, headache or dizziness occur every few days, along with sleep disturbances and loss of appetite. The tests carried out by the Infectious Diseases unit at our children's hospital revealed nothing to account for these worrying symptoms, although they did allow us to rule out certain conditions. To long haulers of all ages, this type of result is all too familiar.

There are also unprocessed emotional traumas for people living with chronic disease. Many long haulers find the one year anniversary of the onset of symptoms to be especially difficult. What I realized in retrospect about the emotional landmine of the covidersary is that a biological trauma can get linked to an association – in this case, a date. This lingering turmoil is an embodied response, not intellectual. I thus had different reactions to the anniversaries of the day on which I last felt well and the day on which my symptoms began.

On the morning of March 25th, I was inexplicably teary. It didn't help that Facebook reminded me of my previous year's posting on that date with smiling photos of Hollis and me skipping stones on a sparkling river while the magnolia trees blossomed, and of walking along limestone ridges in our own bloom of health. I connected this day with grief at the loss of health.

March 26th, however, was linked to anger and resentment. It was complicated, for I felt fortunate to have survived even while I had to acknowledge – almost incomprehensibly – that it had indeed been a full twelve months. I was grateful for all that I had learned on my journey, while also wishing that I had never become ill in the first place. Finally, it was safe to feel frustration and fear because emotions such as these would not pull me under as they would have done when I was weaker. I could address a range of complicated, unconscious emotions at the amount of change in my life and the occasional external pressure to return more quickly to well-being and my "norm," or my pre-pandemic productivity. Resolving these difficult feelings as they surface allows me to return again to a peaceful, healing state. Still, it's an ongoing task, for I have some triggers.

And this brings me to the subject of the vaccine. This week, I am scheduled to receive my second dose of the Moderna vaccine. Like many long haulers, I approach vaccination with a sense of relief at the protection against reinfection (it is a privilege to be in a country where vaccines are accessible) and dread at the possible side effects. At the back of my mind is a small measure of hope because of early studies showing that a minority of long haulers (less than a third) experience some improvement after the Moderna and Pfizer vaccines (see Meinger; no peer-reviewed studies are available at the time of writing). However, the overwhelming emotion for myself and many other long haulers facing the vaccination appointment is, frankly, fear. We know all too well what the symptoms feel like and many in our community report a worsening of their conditions after vaccination, sometimes dangerously so. For me, the headaches lessened after receiving the first dose, but extreme fatigue, a lingering dry cough and sleep disturbances returned. Perhaps the next dose will go better – or not. I don't know. I'm still getting vaccinated.

I share this because there's a danger that the experiences of long COVID are being rendered more invisible in the proliferation of media reports regarding how some long haulers feel better post-vaccine, as if the only thing that a long hauler needs to do is to get vaccinated. Precisely because it's impacting so many people, long COVID stands a chance to raise public and medical awareness for itself as well as for myalgic encephalomyelitis/chronic fatigue syndrome, fibromyalgia, Lyme disease and other conditions where effects can clearly be seen, but tests do not always register what is happening (Ducharme). Visibility can lead to research money, policy changes and general education. The latter can raise awareness of ableism, make clear the need to accept the invisibility of some suffering and head off microaggression (intentional or unintentional forms of discrimination) against ill-being. Shaming and disbelief, I can say from experience, feel like a violence on top of already feeling poorly.

When I began my path to healing, I focused on achieving the label "Survived: Recovered," which made each recovery setback more difficult. My attention now is on being at peace in the present and acknowledging that long COVID time spirals; it waxes and wanes, it moves forward and relapses in no discernable pattern, even in those cases where the general progression is toward increasing health. For me, I have therefore had to learn to measure improvement over spans of months, not in small increments of days and weeks. My daily priorities continue to be caring for my family (including asking for help when needed), pacing myself at work, and finding a way to practice activities that promote a calm and connected state. Rebalancing feels challenging and I don't succeed every day. However, I'm much more likely to do so if I can continue to write creatively, sing, rest as needed and turn to nature even for a little while.

Appendix B | Michigan Tribal Culture

HROUGHOUT my healing, I have found inspiration in the teachings of the Anishinaabek: people who were here long ago, whose descendants are my neighbors and friends, and whom I deeply respect individually and as a living culture. In these pages, I have chosen terminology that I likewise intend to show awareness and respect.

Opinions diverge as to whether Native American or Indian is the preferred name. While the former has become the politically correct option as proposed by the United States government in the third quarter of the twentieth century, I have settled on Indian (except where a quotation or the census uses Native American). At a reading in March 1993, author Sherman Alexie made a powerful case for this referent: "The white man tried to take our land, our sovereignty, and our languages. And he gave us the word 'Indian.' Now he wants to take the word 'Indian' away from us too. Well, he can't have it." A friend who is a citizen of the Little River Band of Ottawa Indians further clarified that being referred to as Native American can raise eyebrows within her community. Indian, as the older term, is what she and her people have been for generations. They do not think to associate it with India, because India isn't part of their culture. "Indian," Valerie summed up, "is always okay."

Mostly, this book specifies the particular tribe or band under discussion, rather than referring to all indigenous peoples of North America. In so doing, it preserves the spellings of tribal names that are closest to how they are pronounced within the tribes. I therefore prefer Odawa and Ojibwe rather than the English equivalents Ottawa and Chippewa, except where the latter are used within titles, as in the Grand Traverse Band of Ottawa and Chippewa Indians. The Odawa and Ojibwe tribes historically resided in and continue to inhabit the county where I grew up, along with neighboring northern and southern counties. The Bodéwadmi homeland is farther south (Potawatomi in English).

These three Michigan tribes have similar cultures and languages, but I have nevertheless had to choose between variants. People from the Odawa, Ojibwe and Bodéwadmi nations all use Anishinaabe ("Original Man") to describe themselves. To make a word plural in the Odawa language, a "k" is added to the end of the word (Wemigwase 6).

The letter "g" functions similarly in Ojibwe. Because an Odawa band mostly lived where my Michigan home is situated, it makes sense to use Anishinaabek when referencing the three tribes found in Michigan.

As I have learned more about Anishinaabek culture and history, my sorrow has deepened for what Indian country has been enduring. Books, documentary films and discussions with friends reveal deep psychological scars, physical abuse, poverty, glass ceilings, and drug and alcohol abuse. Dominant white culture must acknowledge what has happened so that ignorance does not continue to lead to microaggressions. Much recent Indian history and experience is covered up or simply unknown outside of the reservations.

I was appalled and grieved, for example, to learn that the last Indian boarding school operating in the USA was located a couple hours' drive from where I grew up. Across North America, these schools forced children to forget their language, culture, spiritual beliefs and family ties, educating them for working-class life and the military. Holy Childhood of Jesus Boarding School originally began in 1829 as a collaborative effort between Father Peter de Jean and the Odawak in Harbor Springs, Michigan. It closed its doors in 1983 (Stateside), during my freshman year at another boarding school just sixty-six miles away ... only I went by choice and privilege. The fact that Holy Childhood was ongoing during my own schooling horrifies me. Worse, I only learned about it three decades later.

I grew up on Odawa homeland, where I continue to reside alongside enrolled members in local Odawa bands. I was raised by this land, too. And by parents of European descent whose teachings about our connections with the earth resemble many of the ways of the Odawa. This mutual rootedness in place allows for a sort of current to flow among past, present and future inhabitants. One of my friends observed this to me; her culture in Ghana embraces an interconnected world that is not dissimilar to Anishinaabek perceptions of the fluidity of time.

To my way of thinking, we can only begin healing individuals, communities and the earth by seeking to know, to recover, to remind, to apologize and to adjust as needed. This process acknowledges our interconnectivity and responsibility, including across living cultures and to the land itself.

Works Cited

All websites were last accessed in April 2021.

Primary Sources

Angelou, Maya. *On the Pulse of Morning.* New York: Random House, 1993.

"The Appalling Calamity." *New York Herald.* 19 Sept. 1857.

Arnold, Matthew. "Dover Beach." 1867. *Arnold: Poetical Works.* Eds. C.B. Tinker and H.F. Lowry. 1950. London: Oxford UP, 1966. 210–12.

Augustine, Stephen. "Mi'kmaq Creation Story." *Dawnland Voices: An Anthology of Indigenous Writing from New England.* Ed. Siobhan Senier. Lincoln: U of Nebraska P, 2014. 27–8.

Bashō, Matsuo. *Bashō's Haiku: Selected Poems of Matsuo Bashō.* Trans. David Landis Barnhill. Albany: State U of New York, 2004.

Benton-Banai, Edward. *The Mishomis Book: The Voice of the Ojibway.* 1988. Minneapolis: U of Minnesota P, 2010.

Biden, Joseph. [Acceptance Speech.] In "Read Joe Biden's President-Elect Acceptance Speech: Full Transcript." By Matt Stevens. *The New York Times.* 9 Nov. 2020. www.nytimes.com/article/biden-speech-transcript.html.

Blackbird, Andrew J. *History of the Ottawa and Chippewa Indians of Michigan: A Grammar of their Language, and Personal and Family History of the Author.* 1887. Rpt. Petoskey: Little Traverse Regional Historical Society, 1977.

Blake, William. "And did those feet in ancient time." Preface from *Milton: A Poem in Two Books.* 1808. *The Poetical Works of William Blake: Lyrical and Miscellaneous.* Ed. William Michael Rossetti. 1847. London: Bell, 1913. 142.

Browning, Elizabeth Barrett. *Aurora Leigh.* 1850. Ed. and intro. Kerry McSweeney. Oxford: Oxford UP, 1993.

Burne-Jones, Edward Coley. *The Golden Stairs.* 1876–80. Oil paint on canvas. Reference N04005. Tate, London.

—. *Phyllis and Demophoon*. 1870. Body color and watercolor with gold medium and gum arabic on composite layers of paper on canvas. Accession Number 1916P37. Birmingham Museum and Art Gallery.

Carlyle, Thomas. *Past and Present*. London: Chapman and Hall, 1843.

Dante Alighieri. *Inferno*. Intro. Robert Hollander. Trans. Robert and Jean Hollander. New York: Random, 2002.

Dickens, Charles. *Hard Times*. 1854. Ed. and intro. David Craig. London: Penguin, 1969.

—. *The Mystery of Edwin Drood*. 1870. Ed. Arthur J. Cox. Intro. Angus Wilson. London: Penguin, 1993.

Dickinson, Emily. "The Blue Jay." In "Emily Dickinson's Letters." By Thomas Wentworth Higginson. *The Atlantic*. Oct. 1891. www.theatlantic.com/magazine/archive/1891/10/emily-dickinsons-letters/306524/

Dungpo, Su. "Life." *Other People's Thoughts*. Ed. and trans. Simon Leys. Melbourne: Schwartz, 2007. 54.

Eliot, George. *Daniel Deronda*. 4 vols. Edinburgh: Blackwood, 1876.

—. *The Mill on the Floss*. 1860. 2 vols. Cabinet Ed. Edinburgh: Blackwood, 1878.

Ellery Channing, William to Henry David Thoreau. 5 Mar. 1845. Folio 1. *Emerson's Scholar: A Middlebury Tradition*. Interactive online version of the Fall 2003 exhibit. Starr Library, Middlebury College, Vermont. midddigital.middlebury.edu/emerson/transcendentalism/sub/wecchanning/letter.htm.

Farmer, John. "Fair Phyllis I Saw Sitting All Alone." *The First Set of English Madrigals*. London: Barley, 1599.

Forster, E.M. *A Room With a View*. London: Arnold, 1908.

Frost, Robert. "Dedication." Typescript. 1961. Stewart L. Udall Collection. Library of Congress. www.loc.gov/resource/mcc.088/?r=-0.816,0.15,2.633,1.898,0

—. "Two Look at Two." *New Hampshire: A Poem with Notes and Grace Notes*. 1923. New York: Random House, 2019. 95-6.

Gorman, Amanda. *The Hill We Climb: An Inaugural Poem for the Country*. Fwd. Oprah Winfrey. New York: Penguin Random House, 2021.

—. "*The Hill We Climb*: The Amanda Gorman Poem That Stole the Inauguration Show." *The Guardian*. 20 Jan. 2021. www.theguardian.com/us-news/2021/jan/20/amanda-gorman-poem-biden-inauguration-transcript

Hughes, Ted. "Relic." *Collected Poems*. Ed. Paul Keegan. New York: Farrar, Straus and Giroux, 2003. 78.

Joncas, Jan Michael. "On Eagle's Wings." 1979. Words adapted from Psalm 91. Arr. Mark Hayes. Brentwood: Jubilate, 1991.

Jones, William. *Fox Texts.* Vol. 1. Leyden: Brill, 1907.

Mill, John Stuart. *Autobiography.* 1873. Preface John Jacob Coss. New York: Columbia UP, 1924.

"The Moral of the Tamarack's Fall from Grace." *Calgary Herald.* 20 Apr. 2008. www.pressreader.com/canada/calgary-herald/20080420/281835754424904.

Nash, Ogden. "The Chipmunk." *The Best of Ogden Nash.* Ed. Linell Nash Smith. Chicago: Dee, 2007. 183-4.

Noori, Margaret. "Waawaateseg (Fireflies)." *Michigan Quarterly Review.* Special issue on The Great Lakes: Love Song and Lament 50.3 (Summer 2011): 310-11.

Oliver, Mary. "Driving through the Wind River Reservation: A Poem of Black Bear." *Dream Work.* New York: Grove, 1986. 31.

—. "Winter Sleep. *Twelve Moons.* 1972. London: Little, Brown, 1979. 53.

Otto, Simon. *Grandmother Moon Speaks.* Lansing: Thunder Bay P, 1995.

Puccini, Giacomo. *Madama Butterfly.* Libretto by Luigi Illica and Giuseppe Giacosa. 1904. Milan: G. Ricordi, 1907.

Reed, H. Owen. "Michigan Morn: From the Folk-Opera *Michigan Dream.*" Words by John Jennings. Van Nuys: Alfred, 1995.

Schreiner, Olive. *The Story of an African Farm.* 1883. Intro. Dan Jacobson. London: Penguin, 1995.

Shakespeare, William. *The Complete Works of Shakespeare.* Ed. David Bevington. 3rd ed. Glenview: Scott, Foresman, 1980.

Stevenson, Robert Louis. "Winter-Time." *A Child's Garden of Verses.* 1885. Philadelphia: Altemus, [1899]. 89-90.

"A Story about the Crow: Andek." *Ojibwe Language and Culture.* Leech Lake Band of Ojibwe. N.d. ojibwelanguageandculture.weebly.com/a-story-about-the-crow.html.

Tanner, John. *The Falcon.* 1830. Intro. Louise Erdich. London: Penguin, 2003.

Tennyson, Alfred. *In Memoriam A.H.H.* 1850. *Tennyson: A Selected Edition.* 1969. Ed. Christopher Ricks. Rev. Ed. Harlow: Longman, 2007. 331-484.

Thompson, Charles. Design for the Great Seal (obverse side). 1782. National Archives Identifier 595257. i2.wp.com/prologue.blogs.archives.gov/wp-content/uploads/2015/06/00719_2002_001_a.jpg?ssl=1

Thoreau, Henry David. 20 Oct. 1860. *The Writings of Henry David Thoreau: Journal, August 1, 1860–November 3, 1861.* Vol. XIV. Ed. Bradford Torrey. Walden Ed. Boston: Houghton Mifflin, 1906. 155–61.

—. *Walden.* 1854. *The Portable Thoreau.* Ed. Jeffrey S. Cramer. London: Penguin, 2012. 197–468.

"Thriving Center: The Wylie Cooperage Co. at Interlochen Employs 100 Men." *Morning Record* [Traverse City, Michigan]. 20 May 1897. Pg 1. www.newspapers.com/image/?clipping_id=13694803&fcfToken= eyJhbGciOiJIUzI1NiIsInR5cCI6IkpXVCJ9.eyJmcmVlLXZpZX'Xc taWQiOjIwNzA1NzMsImlhdCI6MTYxMDc0ODU3NCwiZXh wIjoxNjEwODM0OTc0fQ.LoRBF5lKIxvQXGhSrP79huUkmk UPnLnyRbML2f0O_Rs.

Tzu, Lao. *Tao Te Ching.* 4 B.C. Trans. D.C. Lau. London: Penguin, 1985.

—. *The Way of Life According to Lao Tzu.* 4 B.C. Trans. Witter Bynner. 1944. New York: Penguin Putnam, 1986.

Whitman, Walt. *Song of Myself.* 1855. Leaves of Grass *and Selected Prose.* Intro. Ellman Crasnow. London: Dent, 1993. 27–80.

Woolf, Virginia. *Orlando: A Biography.* 1928. Ed. Brenda Lyons. Intro. Sandra M. Gilbert. London: Penguin, 1993.

Wordsworth, William. Preface (1800) and "Lines Written a Few Miles above Tintern Abbey, On Revisiting the Banks of the Wye during a Tour. July 13, 1798." *Lyrical Ballads 1798 and 1800.* S.T. Coleridge and William Wordsworth. Eds. Michael Gamer and Dahlia Porter. Ontario: Broadview, 2008. 171–87; 282–6.

Secondary Sources

American Psychological Association. "One Year Later, a New Wave of Pandemic Health Concerns." 11 Mar. 2021. www.apa.org/news/press/releases/stress/2021/one-year-pandemic-stress.

Beresford-Kroeger, Diana. *Arboretum America: A Philosophy of the Forest.* Fwd. Edward O. Wilson. Ann Arbor: U of Michigan P, 2003.

—. *The Global Forest: Forty Ways Trees Can Save Us.* London: Penguin, 2010.

—. "Green Machines." *New Internationalist.* 1 Apr. 2016. newint.org/features/2016/04/01/forest-chemistry.

—. *To Speak for the Trees: My Life's Journey from Ancient Celtic Wisdom to a Healing Vision of the Forest.* Toronto: Random House Canada, 2019.

Bodovski, Katerina. "Why I Collapsed on the Job." *The Chronicle of Higher Education* 14.24 (15 Feb. 2018): 4.

Bright, William. *Native American Placenames of the United States.* Norman: U of Oklahoma P, 2004.

Bugos, Claire. "The Myths of the Thanksgiving Story and the Lasting Damage They Imbue." *Smithsonian Magazine.* 26 Nov. 2019. www.smithsonianmag.com/history/thanksgiving-myth-and-what-we-should-be-teaching-kids-180973655/.

Callard, Felicity. "Epidemic Time: Thinking from the Sickbed." *Bulletin of the History of Medicine.* 94.4 (Winter 2020): 727–43. doi.org/10.1353/bhm.2020.0093.

—. Keynote address, question-and-answer session. Northern Network for Medical Humanities Research Congress 2021 on Medical Humanities: In(visibility). Online, Institute for Medical Humanities, Durham University. 22 Apr. 2021.

Carlson, Scott. "Over Time, Humanities Grads Close the Pay Gap with Professional Peers." *The Chronicle of Higher Education.* 7 Feb. 2018. www-chronicle-com.ezp.slu.edu/article/over-time-humanities-grads-close-the-pay-gap-with-professional-peers/.

Chadd, Rachel Warren and Marianne Taylor. *Birds: Myth, Lore & Legend.* London: Bloomsbury, 2016.

Child, Brenda J. Introduction. *Strength of the Earth: The Classic Guide to Ojibwe Uses of Native Plants.* By Frances Densmore. 1928. St. Paul: Minnesota Historical Society P, 2005. v–xiii.

Cooper, Anderson. "Puzzling, Often Debilitating After-Effects Plaguing COVID-19 'Long-Haulers.'" *60 Minutes.* Prod. Nichole Marks and David M. Levine. CBS. 22 Nov. 2020. www.cbsnews.com/news/COVID-long-haulers-60-minutes-2020-11-22/.

Cosier, Susan. "Self-Isolation is Turning Children into Budding Birders." *Audubon Magazine.* 15 Apr. 2020. www.audubon.org/news/self-isolation-turning-children-budding-birders.

Courchene, Dave. "Our 7 Teachings." *YouTube,* uploaded by Sagkeeng Child & Family Services, Manitoba. 16 May 2014. youtu.be/sASjfNI_lD0

"COVID-19 Rapid Guideline: Managing the Long-term Effects of COVID-19." NICE guideline [NG188]. 18 Dec. 2020. www.nice.org.uk/guidance/ng188.

Crick, Julie. "Trees Provide Historic Navigational Aid." *Michigan State University Extension.* 28 Dec. 2015. www.canr.msu.edu/news/trees_provide_historic_navigation_aid.

Dana, Deb. *The Polyvagal Theory in Therapy: Engaging the Rhythm of Regulation.* New York: Norton, 2018.

David, Nicola. "'Brain fog': The People Struggling to Think Clearly Months after COVID." *The Guardian.* 9 Oct. 2020. www.theguardian.com/world/2020/oct/09/brain-fog-the-people-struggling-to-think-clearly-months-after-COVID

Davis, Hannah E., Gina S. Assaf, Lisa McCorkell, Hannah Wei, et al. "Characterizing Long COVID in an International Cohort: 7 Months of Symptoms and Their Impact." MedRxiv. 27 Dec. 2020. doi.org/10.1101/2020.12.24.20248802

Densmore, Frances. *Strength of the Earth: The Classic Guide to Ojibwe Uses of Native Plants.* 1928. Intro. Brenda J. Child. St. Paul: Minnesota Historical Society P, 2005.

Dhanesha, Neel. "Birdwatching is a Bright Spot in a Pandemic-Stricken Economy." *Audubon Magazine.* 6 Aug. 2020. www.audubon.org/news/birdwatching-bright-spot-pandemic-stricken-economy.

Douglass, John F., Margaret B. Holman and James H. Stephenson. "Paleoindian, Archaic, and Woodland Artifacts from a Site at Green Lake, Grand Traverse County, Michigan." *The Michigan Archaeologist* 44.4 (Dec. 1998): 151–92.

Driscoll, Brighid. "The Story of the Crooked Trees." GTPulse. *9 & 10 News.* 18 Sept. 2020. www.9and10news.com/2020/09/18/gtpulse-the-story-of-the-crooked-trees/.

Ducharme, Jamie. "Have We Been Thinking about Long-Haul Coronavirus All Wrong?" *Time.* 16 Oct. 2020. ti.me/39he8zJ.

Duric, Donna. "Chief's Bonnet Tells a Rich Story of Anishinaabe Culture." Mississaugas of the Credit First Nation. 10 Oct. 2017. mncfn.ca/chiefs-bonnet-tells-a-rich-story-of-anishinaabe-culture/.

Ettawagheshik, Frank. "The Old Indian Trail." Cadillac Area Visitors Bureau. 25 Apr. 2018. cadillacmichigan.com/old-indian-trail-cadillac-to-traverse-city/.

"Facing Up to Long COVID." Editorial. *The Lancet.* 396.10266. 12 Dec. 2020. Pg 1861. doi.org/10.1016/S0140-6736(20)32662-3.

Fauci, Anthony. Comment at Official Press Conference: COVID-19 Conference Highlights. *YouTube,* uploaded by International AIDS Conference. 9 July 2020. Min. 33.19. youtu.be/UMmT48IC0us.

Flaherty, Colleen. "Relying on Women, Not Rewarding Them." *Inside Higher Ed.* 12 Apr. 2017.

www.insidehighered.com/news/2017/04/12/study-finds-female-professors-outperform-men-service-their-possible-professional.

Fontaine, Jerry. *Our Hearts Are as One Fire: An Ojibway-Anishinaabe Vision for the Future.* Vancouver: U of British Columbia P, 2020.

Foucault, Michel. *Discipline and Punish: The Birth of the Prison.* 1975. Trans. Alan Sheridan. 1977. 2nd ed. New York: Random House, 1995.

Fredston, Jill. "A View from Water Level." Cambridge in America Day 2006. *YouTube,* uploaded by Cambridge University. 2 Dec. 2006. youtu.be/QdMmTHuizbI.

French, Martin. "The Prayer Carrier." *So You Should Know / Chi Ki Ken Da Mun.* Eds. Linda North and Barb St. Goddard. Canada: National Literacy Secretariat, 1997. 36. Copian Digital Library, CDÉACF. en.copian.ca/library/learning/chikiken/chikiken.pdf.

Frenzer, Meagan T. "The Great Seal: Celebrating 233 Years of a National Emblem." *Pieces of History: A Blog of the US National Archives.* 20 June 2015. prologue.blogs.archives.gov/2015/06/20/the-great-seal-celebrating-233-years-of-a-national-emblem/.

Geddes, Linda. "Long COVID: Overlap Emerges with ME – Including Debate over Treatment." *The Guardian.* 19 Nov. 2020. www.theguardian.com/world/2020/nov/19/long-COVID-overlap-emerges-with-me-including-debate-over-treatment.

Grandjean, Dominique et al. "Detection Dogs as a Help in the Detection of COVID-19: Can the Dog Alert on COVID-19 Positive Persons by Sniffing Axillary Sweat Samples?" *BioRxiv.* 5 June 2020. doi.org/10.1101/2020.06.03.132134.

Guarino, Cassandra M. and Victor M.H. Borden. "Faculty Service Loads and Gender: Are Women Taking Care of the Academic Family?" *Research in Higher Education* 58 (5 Apr. 2017): 672–94. doi.org/10.1007/s11162-017-9454-2

Hanka, Ladislav R. "Land of the Crooked Tree, L'Arbre Croche, Waganakising." Website. 2005. ladislavhanka.com/Ladislav_Hanka_Etchings/Crooked_Trees_2.html.

Hartle, Paul. "Re: Checking In." E-mail to Phyllis Weliver, 18 Dec. 2020.

—. "Re: Checking In." E-mail to Phyllis Weliver. 28 Dec. 2020.

Heilbrun, Carolyn G. *Writing a Woman's Life.* New York: Norton, 1988.

Henley, Jon. "'Close to 100% accuracy': Helsinki Airport Uses Sniffer Dogs to Detect Covid." *The Guardian.* 24 Sept. 2020.

www.theguardian.com/world/2020/sep/24/close-to-100-accuracy-airport-enlists-sniffer-dogs-to-test-for-COVID-19.

Hunnicutt, Benjamin Kline. *Kellogg's Six-Hour Day.* Philadelphia: Temple UP, 1996.

—. *Work without End: Abandoning Shorter Hours for the Right to Work.* Philadelphia: Temple UP, 1988.

Jabr, Ferris. "The Social Life of Forests." *The New York Times Magazine.* 6 Dec. 2020. www.nytimes.com/interactive/2020/12/02/magazine/tree-communication-mycorrhiza.html?smid=tw-share.

Johnston, Basil. *Ojibway Heritage.* 1976. Lincoln: U of Nebraska P, 1990.

Jung, Carl. *Four Archetypes: Mother, Rebirth, Spirit, Trickster.* Extracted from *The Archetypes and the Collective Unconscious.* Vol. 9, Part I of *Collected Works of C.G. Jung.* Trans. R.F.C. Hull. Fwd. Sonu Shamdasani. Princeton: Princeton UP, 2010.

Kimmerer, Robin Wall. *Braiding Sweetgrass.* Minneapolis: Milkweed, 2013.

Kinder, Gary. *Ship of Gold in the Deep Blue Sea.* New York: Atlantic Monthly P, 1998.

Li, Qing. "Effect of Forest Bathing Trips on Human Immune Function." *Environmental Health Prevention Medicine* 15 (2010): 9–17. doi: 10.1007/s12199-008-0068-3

Lopez, Barry H. *Giving Birth to Thunder, Sleeping with his Daughter: Coyote Builds North America.* 1977. New York: Hearst, 1990.

Maciocia, Giovanni. "Sundays with Giovanni." Host Susan Lange. 10 Ep. *YouTube,* uploaded by Giovanni Maciocia. 9 Apr. 2019. youtube.com/playlist?list=PL2yr1hIh3byvqjWvJTvH4wTo5STo-pW_K.

McClurken, James M. *Our People, Our Journey: The Little River Band of Ottawa Indians.* East Lansing: Michigan State P, 2009.

Meinger, Gez. "2nd Dose Vaccine Reaction Data for Long Covid." *YouTube,* uploaded by RUN-DMC. 24 Mar. 2021. youtu.be/nx03J_7SA4M

Miserandino, Christine. "The Spoon Theory." 2003. ButYouDontLookSick.com.

Murphy, Carrie. "This Is How Joy Affects Your Body." *Healthline.* Upd 22 Aug. 2018. www.healthline.com/health/affects-of-joy.

National Geographic. "A Short Guide to Chipmunk Noises." *YouTube,* uploaded by National Geographic. 12 Jun 2015. youtu.be/ESJaPmfbius.

Nhất Hạnh, Thích. *Teachings on Love.* 1995. Berkeley: Parallax, 2007.

Nikiforuk, Andrew. "'Mother Trees' and Diana Beresford-Kroeger: A Special Relationship." *The Tyee.* 26 Feb. 2020. thetyee.ca/News/2020/02/26/Mother-Trees-Beresford-Kroeger/.

Noodin, Margaret. "Minowakiing: The Good Land." Tedx UW-Milwaukee. 13 Dec. 2017. youtu.be/ddyFh1Rdho4.

Norwood, Arlisha R. "Sarah Hale." National Women's History Museum, 2017. www.womenshistory.org/education-resources/biographies/sarah-hale.

Oxford, John. "Pandemic 1918: Origins, Symptoms and Spread." BBC Radio 4. 15 May 2020. Prod. Ashley Byrne and Iain Mackness. www.bbc.co.uk/programmes/m000j2ty.

Puit, Glenn. "Residents Take Good Care of Bent-Tree Trail Marker." *Traverse City Record Eagle.* 22 Dec. 2012. Upd 19 Aug. 2014. www.record-eagle.com/news/local_news/residents-take-good-care-of-bent-tree-trail-marker/article_7cc32fae-a190-50f5-96bc-dac17e5308a8.html.

Rempel, Zachary. "An Anishinaabe Ethno-Ornithology of Wabaseemoong Independent Nations." 2019. U of Manitoba, MNRM thesis. www.umanitoba.ca/institutes/natural_resources/pdf/2020/Masters%20Thesis%20Rempel%202020.pdf.

Rosenberg, Charles E. "What Is an Epidemic: AIDS in Historical Perspective." *Daedalus.* 118.2 (Spring 1989): 1–17.

Rosenbloom, Stephanie. "Please Don't Make Me Go on Vacation." *New York Times.* 10 Aug. 2006. www.nytimes.com/2006/08/10/fashion/10vacation.html

Samuels, Ellen. "Six Ways of Looking at Crip Time." *Disability Studies Quarterly* 37.3 (Summer 2017). dsq-sds.org/article/view/5824.

Savage, Mark. "The UK Is Streaming Christmas Songs Earlier than Ever." *BBC News.* 13 Nov. 2020. www.bbc.com/news/entertainment-arts-54929909.

Savinelli, Alfred. *Plants of Power: Native American Ceremony and the Use of Sacred Plants.* Summertown: Book Publishing Co., 2002.

Schneider, Nathan. "The Labors of Leisure." *The Chronicle of Higher Education.* 20 Oct. 2014. www.chronicle.com/article/the-labors-of-leisure/.

Schor, Juliet B. *The Overworked American: The Unexpected Decline of Leisure.* New York: HarperCollins, 1991.

Shapiro, Francine and Margot Silk Forrest. *EMDR: The Breakthrough Therapy for Overcoming Anxiety, Stress, and Trauma.* New York: HarperCollins, 1997.

Silverman, David J. *This Land is Their Land: The Wampanoag Indians, Plymouth Colony, and the Troubled History of Thanksgiving.* New York: Bloomsbury, 2019.

Smith, Huron H. "Ethnobotany of the Ojibwe Indians." *Bulletin of the Public Museum of the City of Milwaukee* 4.3 (2 May 1932): 327–525.

Stateside Staff. "A Harbor Springs Boarding School Worked to Erase Odawa Culture until the 1980s." *Michigan Radio.* 8 Nov. 2017. tinyurl.com/y66bg2cc.

Stokstad, Erik. "The Pandemic Stilled Human Activity. What Did This 'Anthropause' Mean for Wildlife?" *Science.* 13 Aug. 2020. doi: 10.1126/science.abe3232

"Survey: Canadians Skip Vacation, Fear Falling Behind at Work." *CBC News.* 3 Sept. 2005. www.cbc.ca/news/technology/survey-canadians-skip-vacation-fear-falling-behind-at-work-1.554774.

"Tap Water Can Add Up to Big Waste." *The San Diego Union-Tribune.* 6 Nov. 2015. www.sandiegouniontribune.com/lifestyle/sdut-saving-water-brushing-teeth-2015nov06-story.html.

Tatera, Kelly. "Scientists Reveal Why 'Forest Bathing' or Going to the Beach Boosts Our Well-Being." *The Science Explorer.* 3 Feb. 2016. thescienceexplorer.com/brain-and-body/scientists-reveal-why-forest-bathing-or-going-beach-boosts-our-well-being.

Treuer, Anton. *Everything You Wanted to Know about Indians but Were Afraid to Ask.* St. Paul: Minnesota Historical Society P, 2012.

Tsunetsugu, Yuko, Bum-Jin Park and Yoshifumi Miyazaki. "Trends in Research Related to 'Shinrin-yoku' (Taking in the Forest Atmosphere or Forest Bathing) in Japan." *Environmental Health and Preventive Medicine* 15.1 (Jan. 2010): 27–37. doi: 10.1007/s12199-009-0091-z

University of East Anglia. "It's Official – Spending Time Outside Is Good for You." ScienceDaily. 6 July 2018. www.sciencedaily.com/releases/2018/07/180706102842.htm

"Vacation Deprivation Up This Year Over Last." Ipsos-Reid Canada. 13 May 2008. www.ipsos.com/en-ca/vacation-deprivation-year-over-last.

Van Gennep, Arnold. *The Rites of Passage.* 1909. Chicago: U of Chicago P, 1960.

Vogel, Virgil J. *Indian Names in Michigan.* Ann Arbor: U of Michigan P, 1986.

Walsh, James D. "How Reliable are COVID-19 Tests?" *Intelligencer.* 10 June 2020. nymag.com/intelligencer/2020/06/how-accurate-are-COVID-19-tests.html

Walsh, L.L. and P.K. Tucker. "Contemporary Range Expansion of the Virginia Opossum (*Didelphis virginiana*) Impacted by Humans and Snow Cover." *Canadian Journal of Zoology* 96.2 (1 Feb. 2018): 107–15. doi: 10.1139/cjz-2017-0071.

Wang Ju-Yi. *Applied Channel Theory in Chinese Medicine: Wang Ju-Yi's Lectures on Channel Therapeutics.* Seattle: Eastland P, 2008.

Weliver, Phyllis. "Coals of Fire and *The Lover's Tale*: The Gladstones and the Tennysons." 2011 Gladstone Lecture. Gladstone's Library, Wales.

—. *Mary Gladstone and the Victorian Salon: Music, Literature, Liberalism.* Cambridge: Cambridge UP, 2017.

—. *The Musical Crowd in English Fiction, 1840–1910: Class, Culture and Nation.* Basingstoke: Palgrave Macmillan, 2006.

Wemigwase, Winnay (ed.) "Our Land and Culture: A 200 Year History of our Land Use." Harbor Springs: Little Traverse Bay Bands of Odawa Indians, 2005.

Wilson, Charles Reagan. Entry for "Opossum." *The New Encyclopedia of Southern Culture.* Vol 8: Environment. Ed. Martin V. Melosi. Chapel Hill: U of North Carolina P, 2007. 256–9.

Witcher, Heather Bozant. "Sympathetic Texts: Collaborative Writing in the Long Nineteenth Century (1814–1909)." Diss. Saint Louis U, 2017.

Made in the USA
Monee, IL
13 March 2022

92862710R00132